David Willcocks is the Director of the Royal College of Music and Musical Director of the Bach Choir. From 1957 until 1974 he was a Fellow and Organist of King's College Cambridge, and directed the famous King's College Choir, whose Festival of Nine Lessons and Carols is broadcast every year throughout the world on Christmas Eve.

CHRISTMAS CAROLS

David Willcocks

SPHERE BOOKS LIMITED
30/32 Gray's Inn Road, London WC1X 8JL

First published in Great Britain by Sphere Books Ltd 1975
Copyright © David Willcocks 1975
Introduction copyright © Alan Kendall 1975
Music drawn by Jon Barkwith

TRADE MARK

Set in Monotype Plantin

Printed in Great Britain by
Hazell Watson & Viney Ltd
Aylesbury, Bucks

INDEX OF TITLES AND FIRST LINES

A CHILD THIS DAY IS BORN	29
A GREAT AND MIGHTY WONDER	30
A MERRY CHRISTMAS	31
A VIRGIN MOST PURE	32
ADESTE FIDELES	72
ALL MY HEART	36
ANGELS FROM THE REALMS	34
AS WITH GLADNESS	37
AWAY IN A MANGER	38
BETHLEHEM OF NOBLEST CITIES	39
BLESSED BE THAT MAID	40
BOAR'S HEAD CAROL	41
CHRIST WAS BORN	42
CHRISTIANS, AWAKE	44
COME ALL YOU WORTHY GENTLEMEN	48
COME LEAVE YOUR SHEEP	46
COVENTRY CAROL	49
DECK THE HALL	50
DING DONG DING!	107
DING DONG! MERRILY ON HIGH	51
GABRIEL'S MESSAGE	52
GOD REST YOU MERRY	53
GOOD KING WENCESLAS	54
HAIL, BLESSED VIRGIN MARY	56
HARK! THE HERALD ANGELS SING	57
HE IS BORN, THE DIVINE CHRIST-CHILD	58
HERE WE COME A-WASSAILING	60
HOW FAR IS IT TO BETHLEHEM?	62
I SAW THREE SHIPS	64
IL EST NE	58
IN DULCI JUBILO	63
IN THE BLEAK MID-WINTER	66
INFANT HOLY, INFANT LOWLY	67
IT CAME UPON THE MIDNIGHT CLEAR	68
KING JESUS HATH A GARDEN	70
LITTLE JESUS, SWEETLY SLEEP	82
LULLY, LULLA, THOU LITTLE TINY CHILD	49
NOW THE HOLLY BEARS A BERRY	83

O COME, ALL YE FAITHFUL 72
O COME, O COME, EMMANUEL 74
O JESUS, SWEET CHILD 75
O LITTLE TOWN OF BETHLEHEM 76
ON CHRISTMAS NIGHT ALL CHRISTIANS SING 90
ON THE FIRST DAY OF CHRISTMAS 98
ONCE IN ROYAL DAVID'S CITY 77
PAST THREE A CLOCK 78
PATAPAN 111
PERSONENT HODIE 88
QUELLE EST CETTE ODEUR AGREABLE? 109
QUEM PASTORES LAUDAVERE 86
QUITTEZ, PASTEURS 46
REJOICE AND BE MERRY 80
REMEMBER, O THOU MAN 81
ROCKING 82
SANS DAY CAROL 83
SEE AMID THE WINTER'S SNOW 84
SHEPHERDS LEFT THEIR FLOCKS 86
SILENT NIGHT 87
SING ALOUD ON THIS DAY 88
SING LULLABY 95
SUSSEX CAROL 90
THE ANGEL GABRIEL FROM HEAVEN CAME 52
THE BOAR'S HEAD IN HAND BEAR I 41
THE FIRST GOOD JOY THAT MARY HAD 96
THE FIRST NOWELL 92
THE HOLLY AND THE IVY 94
THE INFANT KING 95
THE SEVEN JOYS 96
THE THREE KINGS 102
THE TWELVE DAYS OF CHRISTMAS 98
THIS ENDRIS NIGHT 100
THREE KINGS FROM PERSIAN LANDS 102
TOMORROW SHALL BE MY DANCING DAY 105
UNTO US IS BORN A SON 106
UP! GOOD CHRISTEN FOLK 107
WE THREE KINGS 108
WE WISH YOU A MERRY CHRISTMAS 31
WHENCE IS THAT GOODLY FRAGRANCE? 109
WHILE SHEPHERDS WATCHED 110
WILLIE, TAKE YOUR LITTLE DRUM 111

FOREWORD

All the carols and Christmas hymns contained in this book have become popular over the years and have stood the test of time. No attempt has been made to introduce new carols.

Some carols appear in their original form; others have been specially arranged for this book. In making the arrangements my aim has been simplicity, since there are already in existence some good carol books containing elaborate settings suitable for large choirs with or without organ or orchestral accompaniment.

Each of the hymns and carols in this book can be sung unaccompanied by four or more voices, or sung by solo voice with piano, or played on the piano alone.

I hope therefore that the book will be especially useful for carol-singing parties, for use in schools, and for those who wish to make music in the home.

I am very grateful to Alan Kendall for writing the introduction; to Jon Barkwith for drawing the music; and acknowledge permission to reproduce the following carols: *Blessed be that maid*: words by permission of A. R. Mowbray & Co.; *Ding dong ! merrily on high*: words by permission of the Society for Promoting Christian Knowledge; *Hail, blessed Virgin Mary*: words and melody by permission of the Faith Press Ltd; *How far is it to Bethlehem ?*: words by permission of Mrs D. E. Collins and A. P. Watt Ltd; *Infant holy, infant lowly*: words from *Kingsway Carol Book* by Edith Reed by permission of Evans Brothers Ltd; *In the bleak mid-winter*: words and music from the *English Hymnal* by permission of Oxford University Press; *King Jesus hath a garden*: words and melody by permission of A. R. Mowbray & Co.; *Little Jesus, sweetly sleep*: translation and melody from *The Oxford Book of Carols* by permission of Oxford University Press; *On Christmas night*: words and melody by permission of Mrs R. Vaughan Williams and Oxford University Press; *Past three a clock*: words by permission of the Society for Promoting Christian Knowledge; *Personent hodie*: translation from *The Oxford Book of Carols* by permission of Oxford University Press; *Quem pastores*: translation by permission of G. & I. Holst Ltd and Oxford University Press; *Quittez, pasteurs*: translation by permission of Oxford University Press; *Silent night*: translation by permission of Oxford University Press; *The three kings*: translation and arrangement by permission of Oxford University Press; *The twelve days of Christmas*: melody by permission of Novello & Co.; *Unto us is born a Son*: words and melody by permission of A. R. Mowbray & Co.; *Whence is that goodly fragrance?*: words of verses 1–3 by permission of the Master and Fellows of Magdalene College Cambridge; *Willie, take your little drum*: translation from *The Oxford Book of Carols* by permission of Oxford University Press.

DAVID WILLCOCKS
London, 1975

CHRISTMAS CAROLS

On Advent Sunday, the Christian Church begins its preparations for the celebration of Christmas. At King's College Cambridge, this day is marked by a carol service which begins in almost total darkness, but gradually the choir moves in procession from west to east, from 'darkness to light'. First, from the west, the responsory of ancient Matins on Advent Sunday announces the hope of the Messiah and is followed by the hymn of St Ambrose, *Veni, Redemptor gentium*. As the procession passes into the choir, prophetic lessons alternate with carols. Finally, in the sanctuary, the gospel replaces the prophets. After the blessing the procession retires, as if going to Bethlehem to greet the new light in the world, Jesus Christ.

The theme of Jesus as the Sun of Righteousness is present in one of the most popular of all Christmas carols, *Hark! the herald angels sing* (page 57). The conflict between darkness and light, however, is much older and more universal than Christianity. Even so, within the context of Christmas it was especially fitting that the new sun should eclipse the old as Christianity became the official religion of the Roman Empire.

Doubtless the proximity of the day chosen for the birthday of Christ to the Saturnalia (the festival fell on 17 December) helped to fix Christmas as essentially a time of merriment. Originally the Saturnalia was – or rather were, since the word is plural – a feast to celebrate the end of the autumn sowing, and had many of the characteristics of a harvest home. Gifts were exchanged, and gambling was officially permitted. Slaves wore the pileus, the badge of the free man, were given complete freedom of speech, and attended a banquet dressed in their masters' clothes, the masters waiting on them in rooms decked with evergreens.

To Saturnus, in whose honour the festival was held, was attributed by the people of Latium the introduction of agriculture and the arts of civilized life into their land. The Saturnalia meant therefore a doubly appropriate time for relaxation and rejoicing. The law courts and schools were closed for the duration of the feast and public business was prohibited. People left off the heavy toga, and wore instead a loose gown known as a synthesis, wearing the pileus on their heads. The streets were filled with people shouting 'Io saturnalia'.

Often a mock king was elected at private celebrations, a tradition which is reflected by the Epiphany *galette* custom still observed in France. Epiphany, in the Western Church, commemorates the appearance of Jesus Christ to the Gentiles. On the night before Epiphany – Twelfth Night – the people eat *galettes*, flat cakes of sweetened ruff-puff pastry, into which a bean or tiny doll has been inserted. Whoever finds the doll in his portion is automatically king, puts on the gilded cardboard crown kindly supplied by the bakery with the *galette*, and elects a consort for the rest of the meal. Whenever he drinks, the company must shout '*Le roi boit !*' and raise their glasses and drink also.

From Rome the observance of Christmas spread throughout the West, and although for a long time in the East the feast of the Epiphany was the more important celebration, the Church of Jerusalem abandoned it in favour of Christmas in 549, and only the Armenian Church has failed to do so to this day.

As Christianity moved northwards and westwards across Europe, Christmas had to overcome strong opposition from other pagan celebrations, such as the northern Yule festival and the traditions of the Celts, especially in Britain. There were, for example, pagan festivals held in honour of the sun's rebirth after the winter solstice, which found an echo in the concept of Jesus Christ as the Sun of Righteousness. Yule itself was a Norse winter fire festival, presided over by the god Odin. The surviving tradition of the Yule log at Christmas relates directly to this feast. The log was borne into the house with great ceremony on Christmas Eve, sometimes with a girl seated on it. It had to be kindled with a portion of the previous year's Yule log, specially retained for the purpose. In this way the Yule kindling became a domestic symbol of regeneration and fertility, and was supposed to keep away the angel of death for the ensuing year.

The association of the boar, and the traditional boar's head, with Christmas also stems from this source. As well as being a mighty and dangerous animal, in fact 'a sovereign beast' in the words of the carol, the boar was a symbol of fertility. There was an old saying in Germany that when the corn waved, it was because the boar was rushing through it. The last sheaf of the harvest was saved, and a loaf was made from it in the shape of a boar, and put on the Yule table. It was then kept until the spring sowing, when part of it was eaten and the rest mixed with the seed corn to ensure a good crop. Yuletide, with its tradition of eating and drinking – especially in Scandinavia – was not simply a time for rejoicing, but also for looking ahead to a good year for the crops, and for peace in the land.

Evergreen decorations played a similarly symbolic role in the midwinter festivities, since the gathering of green branches at the winter solstice ensured the rebirth of crops and vegetation the following spring.

So the observance of Christmas, told with simplicity in the gospels, gradually assimilated a whole wealth of detail over the centuries to result in the festival we now know. In that festival music has always played a fundamental role.

Man's use of music and dancing in his rituals is almost as old as the rituals themselves. As far as the biblical roots of Christian tradition are concerned, we read in Samuel II, 6, that when David brought the Ark to Zion he danced before the Lord, but his wife reproved him for so shamelessly uncovering himself. Although she remained barren as a result of her strictures, her attitude was to become that of the Early Church which fought tirelessly to suppress dancing and other pagan customs.

The monk Goscelin, in his *Life of St Edith*, describes a curious incident which apparently took place at Kölbigk in Saxony, around 1020, and which well illustrates what the Church was up against. The pilgrim Theodoric is the narrator:

> On Christmas Eve twelve of us gathered at the Church of
> St Magnus in Kölbigk. . . . We joined hands and danced in the
> churchyard; Gerleuus, as Vorsänger, gave out the fatal
> song . . . .When the priest called to us to stop dancing and
> come to the service, we refused, and the priest invoked the
> wrath of God through the influence of St Magnus. The curse
> took effect, and we found that we could not break the circle or
> stop dancing for a whole year. The priest's son Azo attempted
> to pull his sister Ava out of the ring but only tore away her
> arm, which did not bleed.
>   Meanwhile we danced and leapt and clapped, mocking our
> own pain with the refrain of our song . . . . We neither ate nor
> drank nor slept, and our hair and nails did not grow. People
> flocked to see us, and the Emperor Henry attempted to have a
> shelter built over us, but each night the work was thrown down.
> Finally on the next Christmas Eve the curse was lifted, and we
> went into the church and slept three days, but Ava died and her
> father soon after. Now we wander separately through all
> countries, marked by the agitation of our limbs.

In the Bodleian Library at Oxford there is a fifteenth-century manuscript which shows shepherds dancing at Christ's Nativity. This conveys a more sedate impression of a ring dance than that left by the Kölbigk account, and it is this ring or round dance – also known as a *carole* – that is so important in the development of Christmas carols.

Right up to the time of the Reformation the Church issued edict after edict, and preachers poured out their wrath and scorn from the pulpit in an attempt to induce their listeners to change their ways. Even after that time, dancing and carolling continued to be regarded with suspicion as a relic of Papistry in Protestant societies. The Aberdeen Kirk Sessions Records for 1574 show that fourteen women were charged with 'the playing, dancing and singing of filthy carols on Yule Day, at even, and on Sunday at even, thereafter'. There was a much more serious objection to the dancing of the carol, namely that it had deep-rooted connections with pagan ritual and witchcraft.

In the famous North Berwick witch trials of 1590 it was reported that one Barbara Napier met up with the local witches at the church, 'where she danced endlong the kirkyard, and Gelie Duncan played on a trump; John Fian, masked, led the ring; Agnes Sampson and her daughters and all the rest following the said Barbara to the number of seven score persons'. A feature of the witches' dance was that they faced outwards, and so by moving to the left they moved widdershins, or in the opposite direction to the sun. As with the Black Mass, the doing of exact opposites was a sign of witchcraft, of Black, as opposed to White Magic.

Soon the Puritans were to abolish Christmas altogether as a relic of superstition. To them superstition was synonymous with the Church of Rome. What they were really fighting against, however, was what the Church had battled with for centuries, namely man's atavism in the ritual of the dance.

The world of the Middle Ages was one of naïvety, spontaneity and proximity to nature, where the contrast between silence and sound, darkness and light, like that between summer and winter, was more strongly marked than it is in our own. In such a world, it is not surprising that the Bible stories appeared all the more vivid to people. The Nativity in particular caught the medieval imagination, and produced a stream of lullabies and carols. The shepherd Wat, in a manuscript belonging to Balliol College Oxford, goes to Bethlehem to see the new-born child, and in a scene very reminiscent of the scene in the York cycle of mystery plays makes his own offering to Jesus:

> *When Wat to Bedlem came was,*
> *He sweat; he had gone faster than a pace.*
> *He found Jesus in a simple place*
> *Between an ox and an ass.*
> *With hoy !*
> *For in his pipe he made so much joy.*
>
> *'Jesu, I offer to thee here my pipe,*
> *My skirt, my tarbox, and my scrip;*

Home to my fellows now will I skip,
And also look unto my sheep.'
With hoy ! etc.

'Now, farewell, mine own herdsman Wat.'
'Yay, for God, lady, even so I hat.
Lull well Jesu in thy lap,
And farewell, Joseph, with thy round cap.'
With hoy ! etc.

Wat had rushed to Bethlehem, so he arrived sweating. As the three kings were to make offerings, so he had to, despite the fact that all he had to offer were the very necessities for his calling. The Virgin called him by his name, and he took a tender farewell of St Joseph in his round cap. Such details give the listener a powerful sense of immediacy.

Even carols dealing with more abstract subjects had the same directness of approach. For example, *Adam lay ybounden* muses on the fall of man through the taking of the apple in the Garden of Eden, and the need for redemption as a result, but comes to the conclusion:

Né had the apple taken been,
The apple taken been,
Né had never our lady
A-been heavené queen.

Blessed be the time
That apple taken was.
Therefore we moun singen
Deo gracias!

The fall of man therefore became a matter for thanksgiving because it enabled Our Lady to become Queen of Heaven and necessitated Christ's birth and man's redemption.

As the medieval world prepared for the long winter ahead, Christmas was a marvellous feast on which to concentrate its love of ritual and pageantry. Processions took place both inside and outside the Church, on secular as well as religious occasions, and though the idea of a procession with carols such as is common today has little or no foundation in the liturgy of the medieval Church, carols were often sung, and paid for, throughout Christmas week. As the last Prior of Worcester before the Reformation noted in his accounts for 1520:

> '*Item: rewards for carols on Christmas Day at dinner, 14d.,*
> *at supper, 8d.*
> *Item: to carols upon St John's day, 8d., 2d., 8d.*
> *Item: rewarded to William the Luter for his singing and*
> *playing in the Christmas week,* nil hic.'

Can William really have been such a bad performer as to deserve nothing at all?

Whatever the ultimate derivation of the word carol – and there are still various schools of thought on the matter – there was, as already mentioned, a round dance common throughout Europe in the Middle Ages known as the *carole*. There were several versions of it, but its fundamental characteristic, so important for the development of the Christmas carol as we know it, was the alternation between stanza and burden. The stanza was sung by a soloist – the *Vorsänger* of the Kölbigk incident – whereas the burden was sung by everyone and repeated after every stanza. Indeed, the purists maintain that anything not adhering to this arrangement is not, strictly speaking, a carol. Nowadays we think of a carol as being any kind of song for Christmas, but in view of its evolution, it would be as well to bear in mind the fact that in origin a carol was closely allied to the dance, and that it might celebrate any sort of occasion, sacred or secular.

As we have seen, the Church tried to suppress the dance element, but later decided that the best way of dealing with it was to assimilate it. In this way a very basic dynamic force was harnessed, so that it soon became a powerful weapon in the Church's armoury. Secular tunes were used for religious texts and secular texts were adapted for religious use by direct parody of the words, so that a celebration of profane love became one of divine love. Secular verse forms, well known to the people at large, were used for religious purposes so that they were easily picked up by ear at a time when most people could neither read nor write.

The earliest published collection of carols in England was that of Wynken de Worde in 1521, but the earliest extant reference in this country to carols in literature is found much earlier in a text of 1300, *Cursor mundi*, a poem in Northern Middle English which tells what is basically Bible history from the Creation onwards. Thereafter references become more numerous, as in Chaucer, for example, and the carol continued to flourish until about 1550 when, abruptly, with the onset of the Reformation, the true carol ceased to appear. Hymns and poems on a specifically Christmas theme continued to be written and set to music. The Reformation therefore makes a convenient point up to which one may consider the early carol and the various influences and traditions which brought it to its final flowering in the sixteenth century.

One of the reasons why carols became so popular was the fact that, unlike liturgical texts, they could accommodate change and assert their independence from orthodox theology and canonical history. A typical example of this sort of carol would be *I saw three ships* (page 64) – not that this one involves much theology or history.

But if the liturgical texts themselves could not be changed, other texts might, or at least provide starting points for new carols. Such texts are the antiphons, tropes, sequences and proses. Some of the most famous antiphons are those found towards the end of Advent in the days leading up to Christmas, sung before and after the psalms and canticles: in other words before and after the Magnificat and Nunc dimittis, for example, at Evensong.

A trope was a series of words added to the text of the mass or office by way of amplification or embellishment, which tended to go out of use during the twelfth century, when the trope was replaced by the sequence. Tropes were not finally abolished, however, until 1570, when Pope Pius V revised the Missal. The sequence (which might also be called a prose) was sung between the gradual and the gospel at the mass, and came to resemble a hymn. *Of the Father's love begotten* was originally a trope, also used sometimes as a sequence, to the words of the sanctus, written by a Spaniard in the fourth century and translated by J. M. Neale in the nineteenth century. Another famous sequence or prose is the one for Christmas Day which was eventually turned into *O come, all ye faithful* (page 72).

One must bear in mind that only a certain proportion of the carols were Nativity carols, and that there were others for different Church feasts, as well as a whole host of secular carols on subjects ranging from love to politics. There is a delightful little carol by William Cornish, who was Master of the Chapel Royal under Henry VII and Henry VIII, which is simply an expression of joy and thanksgiving for God's creation:

> *Pleasure it is/To hear, I wis,*
> *The birdes sing./The deer in the dale,*
> *The sheep in the vale,/The corn springing;*
> *God's purveyance/For sustenance*
> *It is for man./Then we always*
> *To him give praise,/And thank him then.*

One reason why the Nativity carols are more in evidence than almost all the others put together is that Christmas was a time of communal feasting and rejoicing par excellence, and it was at feasts and similar occasions that carols were sung, thus fulfilling their essentially social function. At Easter in the earlier centuries there was simply not the food available after the long winter for much feasting.

We gather some idea of what the Christmas feast meant to medieval people after the fast period of Advent from one of the carols of James Ryman, dating from the late fifteenth century.

> *Farewell Advent; Christmas is come;*
> *Farewell from us both all and some.*
>
> *While thou hast been within our house*
> *We ate no puddings nor no souse,*
> *But stinking fish not worth a louse;*
> *Farewell from us both all and some.*
>
> *Our bread was brown, our ale was thin,*
> *Our bread was musty in the bin,*
> *Our ale sour or we did begin;*
> *Farewell from us both all and some.*

Another carol, the *Boar's Head Carol*, gives an idea of the feast itself. The most famous one is that sung at the Queen's College Oxford on Christmas Day every year. The hall is decorated with holly, ivy and laurel above the pictures and around the walls, and over the Provost's chair is a bunch of mistletoe. Usually a fire is lit in the large open fireplace at the side of the hall, so the spirit of medieval Christmas is very much present.

When it is time for dinner, the Provost leads a procession of the Fellows in residence and their guests into the hall and the Latin grace is said. Meanwhile, a second procession has been forming up outside the hall and in the buttery, consisting of the singers and the servants who carry on their shoulders the boar's head on its massive silver salver. The man appointed to sing the solo part in the carol is known as the taberdar, and when the trumpeter has sounded his silver trumpet twice, the taberdar leads the second procession into the hall. In true carol fashion the stanza is sung as a solo and the burden is sung as a chorus as the procession slowly moves up the hall. When the carol is finished, the salver with the boar's head is lowered into position on the table in front of the Provost, who takes the ornaments and decorations from the salver and presents them to the singers and guests. The soloist or taberdar for the year receives the orange from the boar's mouth. When the ceremony has ended dinner begins, and the last verse of the carol with its specific reference to the college – *Reginensi Atrio* – is especially apt.

> *Our steward hath provided this,/In honour of the King of Bliss,*
> *Which on this day to be served is,/*In Reginensi Atrio,
> Caput apri defero,/Reddens laudes Domino.

Another famous version in the Porkington manuscript, dating from the fifteenth century, goes further into the menu:

> *Hey, hey, hey !*
> *The boar's head is armed gay.*
>
> *Then comes in the second course with mickle pride,*
> *The cranes and the herons, the bitterns by their side,*
> *The partridges and the plovers, the woodcocks and the snipe,*
> *With hey !*

The next verse has larks 'in hot stew' for the ladies to pick, and some of the different drinks that might be served, and the meal would be rounded off with 'raisins of Corinth, with other spices more'. Pride of place, however, went to 'the boar's head with mustard armed so gay'.

Another aspect of the medieval Christmas celebrated by the carols is the custom of decorating houses and churches with evergreens. There are carols to both holly and ivy, and the significance of these two in particular stretches back to pagan times. Generally, holly is regarded as the male element and ivy the female. Attempts were made to sanctify their connection with the Christmas season by including them in the words of some carols, as in one found in a manuscript at St John's College Cambridge where the letters IVE(Y) are made to stand for Jesus, Virgin and Emmanuel. A carol generally thought to be by King Henry VIII makes the two a symbol of united love.

> *As the holly groweth green/And never changeth hue,*
> *So I am, ever hath been,/Unto my lady true.*
>
> *As the holly groweth green,/With ivy all alone,*
> *When flowers cannot be seen,/And greenwood leaves be gone.*
>
> *Now unto my lady/Promise to her I make,*
> *From all other only/To her I me betake.*

One might be forgiven for feeling that this, from the hand of a man married six times, sounds rather ironic.

The Christmas spirit continued well into the Tudor age. But already the tide of reform had turned and erosion began to set in. In 1542 Henry VIII abolished one of the more quaint medieval customs, namely the election of boy bishops. In many monasteries, schools and even country parishes, a boy was elected on St Nicholas's Day (6 December), to carry out various duties in the church that were normally the prerogative of the bishop. He remained 'in office' until Holy Innocents' Day (28 December), and the idea behind the practice was to show the value placed in the gospels on the child-like spirit of the Christian.

Although Mary Tudor revived the custom and people said 'St Nicholas yet goeth about the City', Elizabeth eventually abolished it once more. She was too concerned about the episcopacy as a support for the monarchy to allow it to be so playfully used. It was a sign of the times that the naïvety of the medieval mind had given way to political expediency.

No consideration of the early carol can be undertaken without reference to the French *noël* or the Franciscan movement. The *noël* was exclusively connected with Christmas, whereas the English carol, as we have seen, was not always either for Christmas or necessarily religious in content. The *noël* has no metrical form by which it may be distinguished, and although it was written to dance tunes, it has no connection with the *carole* or round dance. Moreover, its development came late in the fifteenth century, at a time when the carol was well established in England. Even so, France has given us some of our favourite carols. *Angels from the realms of glory* (page 34) is an old French tune sung to the words we still use today, which are by J. Montgomery (1771–1854). *Ding dong! merrily on high* (page 51) is also French, and the words are by G. R. Woodward. The tune is that of a dance known as a *branle*, which was the equivalent of our word 'brawl'. *Whence is that goodly fragrance?* (page 109) also came to us from the French.

Going further south, the Basque people have given us a number of beautiful carols, two of which are found here: *The Infant King* (page 95) and *The angel Gabriel* (page 52). In both carols the words are the work of Sabine Baring-Gould (1834–1924).

Traditionally, St Francis of Assisi is attributed with the making of the first crib at Greccio in 1223, some three years before his death, though there is evidence that the custom began earlier. Certainly within a century the practice spread and developed so that we read an account of the crib ceremonies at Rouen in the fourteenth century, where the crib was placed behind the altar, the shepherds entered through the main gates of the choir, and a child on a raised platform acted the part of the angel. Two priests 'of the first rank' were vested in dalmatics and stood by the crib to represent the midwives.

These dramatic representations of biblical scenes brought the mystery play into being, which provided yet another impetus to the development of Christmas carols as we know them. The York and Towneley plays date from the mid-fourteenth century, the Chester plays from about 1400, and the Coventry plays from the first half of the fifteenth century. They were a great stimulus to the writing of Christmas songs, and the *Coventry Carol* (page 49), though the tune in its present form is late sixteenth-century, was written especially for plays that had been performed before Margaret of Anjou, Richard III and Henry VII.

We owe much of the medieval spirit of Christmas that survives today to the Franciscans. As far as the carols themselves are concerned, it was really the Franciscan spirit, rather than any particular lyric form employed, that was so important in the development of the English carol, particularly in the earlier period.

James Ryman, who flourished around 1492, was one of the few English writers known to have been influenced by the Franciscans. Ryman was not highly thought of as a poet and the popularity of his songs was more likely due to the showmanship of the Franciscan friars who introduced them.

When the monks and friars departed, the religious carol suffered badly. The non-religious carol went out of favour too, certainly among the more educated classes, though something very similar survived in the ayres and balletts which next came into favour, along with the madrigal. The carol embarked upon a new phase of its existence, but the old one was by no means gone beyond recall, and in many cases weathered the storms of three centuries.

New music came at this time from Tye, Tallis and Byrd, whose working lives spanned the whole period of reform. The new rite called for music that was worlds apart from that of the old, and the expression of religious sentiment seemed, for some time to come, to be in danger of being confined to four-square idioms. From this period we have the tune for the *Coventry Carol* (page 49), dating in its present form from 1591, set to words from the previous century from the pageant of the Shearmen and Tailors of Coventry. There is also the tune from Este's Psalter of 1592 known as *Winchester Old*, which has been almost irretrievably associated with the words *While shepherds watched*, though these are of much later date.

The nature of the Christmas festival in the pre-Commonwealth period was strongly influenced by Tudor and medieval traditions, though many of the more 'enlightened' people were beginning to feel that things had gone too far. Indeed, if one reads accounts of entertainments at the court of James I, they seem to have been merely an excuse for a vast amount of expenditure. The first Christmas that James and his Danish queen spent in England was kept at Hampton Court, on a scale that had not been seen before. There were sword dances and masques, and on 1 January 1604 a play called *Robin Goodfellow* was performed. But it was chiefly the masques which were the cause of the extravagance. Queen Anne developed a passion for them, and on 8 January that year she and her ladies took the leading parts in *The Vision of the Twelve Goddesses*, staged in the great hall at Hampton Court. The estimated cost was between £2,000 and £3,000, despite the fact that many of the costumes had been improvised out of petticoats from Queen Elizabeth's wardrobe, with loose mantles thrown over them.

For an idea of Christmas entertainment further down the social scale, we can turn to Nicholas Breton's *Fantastickes* of 1626. Breton was the son of a London merchant, and was a poet and satirist of prolific output. His *Fantastickes* contains his observations on men and manners, according to the seasons of the year. There is a slight feeling of tongue-in-cheek as he describes the various aspects of Christmas, as if he too felt that things had gone too far, but in the end he decides that Christmas is a desirable institution:

> *It is now Christmas, and not a cup of drink must pass without a carol; the beasts, fowl and fish come to a general execution and the corn is ground to dust for the bakehouse, and the pastry. Cards and dice purge many a purse, and the youth shew their agility in shoeing of the wild mare. . . . The Lord of Misrule is no mean man for his time, and the guests of the high table must lack no wine. . . . Musicians now make their instruments speak out, and a good song is worth the hearing. In sum, it is a holy time, a duty in Christians for the remembrance of Christ, and a custom among friends for the maintenance of good fellowship. In brief, I thus conclude of it: I hold it a memory of the heaven's love and the world's peace, the mirth of the honest, and the meeting of the friendly.*

Times were soon to change. In 1644 Christmas Day had to be kept as a fast because it fell on the last Wednesday of the month, and the Long Parliament had decreed that each such monthly fast would be held irrespective of the day. Three years later Christmas, along with other festivals, was abolished altogether. And yet it was hard to stamp out, because it was found necessary to repeat the injunction in a resolution of Parliament in 1652: 'That the markets be kept tomorrow, being the five and twentieth day of December. That no observation shall be had of the five and twentieth day of December commonly called Christmas Day; nor any solemnity used or exercised in churches upon that day in respect thereof. . . .'

Of course there were protests. The next year a pamphlet called *The Vindication of Christmas* appeared. The title page shows Christmas as an old man saying 'O Sir, I bring good cheer'. The ordinary man welcomes him 'Old Christmas, welcome; do not fear'. The soldier, however, draws his sword, saying 'Keep out, you come not here'. The pamphleteer laments 'The manner how our high and mighty Christmas Ale, that formerly would knock down Hercules and trip up the heels of a giant, [was] struck into deep consumption with a blow from Westminster'.

For the other side, Hezekiah Woodward in his tract of 1656 called Christmas Day 'The old heathen's feasting day, in honour of Saturn his idol-god, the papist's massing day, the profane man's ranting day, the superstitious man's idol day, the multitude's idle day, Satan's – that adversary's – working day, the true Christian man's fasting day. . . . We are persuaded, no one thing more hindereth the gospel work all the year long, than doth the observation of that idol day once in a year, having so many days of cursed observation with it'.

Happily such a state of affairs could not last long. The monarchy was restored, and by 1660 Samuel Pepys was looking forward to having his house free of workmen before Christmas, the church pews were decked with rosemary and bay – both good in popular lore for withstanding the assault of witches, devils and storms – and a turkey was being roasted in the kitchen.

It is hardly surprising that in such an atmosphere, following the blows that the Reformation dealt to Christmas music in general, little or no new carols emerged. The Thirty Years' War that ravaged Germany, and the Civil War in England, with the Puritan interregnum, disrupted life to catastrophic degrees. Some things have survived, nonetheless. From Germany at this time comes *O little one sweet*, and from Italy *Hail, blessed Virgin Mary*, arranged by Charles Wood and translated by G. R. Woodward. As far as England was concerned, however, the carol did not develop along the freer lines of an ayre or ballett, but more as a hymn, and it was Nahum Tate's metrical version of St Luke II, 8–14, – *While shepherds watched* (page 110) – that was to set the new pattern.

There may not be a great deal for which to thank the latter part of the seventeenth century as far as the carol is concerned, but we must bear in mind that it was a difficult time for the Church, and the age produced some fine hymns which we still sing. The most important thing was that Christmas stayed alive in men's hearts. In the accounts of Lord Leicester's hospital at Warwick for 1660–1661, the year of the Restoration, we read that 6d. was given to 'Mr Green's man' for bringing a cake which they put towards their wassail, and in 1662 Samuel Pepys recorded in his diary how he went to Whitehall on Christmas Day: 'The sermon done, a good Anthemne followed, with vialls; and then the King came down to receive the Sacrament, but I stayed not. . . .' His wife had not been well, but when he returned home, he dined by her bedside 'with great content, having a mess of brave plum-porridge and a roasted pullett for dinner; and I sent for a mince-pie abroad, my wife not being well to make any herself yet'. The spirit of Christmas had weathered yet another storm.

The tradition of good cheer and generosity at Christmas that returned to England with the Restoration of the monarchy continued into the eighteenth century. We get some idea of what was expected of the more well-to-do from a letter written by Horace Walpole in 1748 from his Gothick villa at Strawberry Hill, Twickenham – then in the heart of rural Middlesex. 'Did you ever know a more absolute country gentleman? Here am I come down to what you call keeping Christmas! Indeed it is not in all the forms; I have stuck no laurel and holly in my windows, I eat no turkey and chine, I have no tenants to invite. I have not brought a single soul with me.'

By lamenting the way in which he was failing to keep Christmas, Walpole shows what most people of his class would have been doing, and it was to vary surprisingly little for almost the next two hundred years, when the State made private benefaction unfashionable, if not in fact impossible, and Christmas became a commercial venture.

One must bear in mind that England's was still a largely agricultural economy in the eighteenth century, and that for the majority of people most manufactured goods, let alone imported foods, were beyond their pockets. Christmas was therefore a time when they enjoyed fare that they might well not see for the rest of the year. In this respect, the significance of the contrast between Christmas and the rest of the year puts them much closer to their medieval ancestors who lived some three and four hundred years before them, than to us, a mere two centuries later.

The traditional carols were largely ignored by the sophisticated at this time, but they continued to be sung in country places. Parson James Woodforde recorded how on 24 December 1764, when he was a scholar of New College Oxford, '. . . the bursars gave us scholars eight bottles of port wine to drink at dinner time. They likewise gave us a quarter of a Cheshire cheese'.

When he was in his first parish, we read that '. . . the new singers came very late this evening, and they sang a Christmas carol and an anthem, and they had cyder as usual and o. 2. o. The old singers did not come at all, and I have heard that they have given it over'. Oliver Goldsmith, in 1766, tells how the people of the parish of the Vicar of Wakefield 'kept up the Christmas carol'. Two years later, James Woodforde wrote: 'It being Christmas Eve we had the New Singers of C. Cary this evening at the parsonage, and they having been at great expenses in learning to sing, my father and myself gave them double what we used to do, and therefore instead of one shilling we each gave o. 2. o.' Next year, however, they incurred his displeasure with their singing of Psalm 12 in the New Version, so that when they came to sing on Christmas Eve, he wrote '. . . after giving them a lecture concerning their late behaviour in church, on promise of amendment gave o. 2. o.'

The annual rounds of the parish church choir certainly brought pleasure to many people in country districts, though the choirs themselves might well be a source of annoyance to the local incumbent. The scene recorded above by Parson Woodforde was paralleled by one that Thomas Hardy came to write in his novel *Under the Greenwood Tree*. The minstrels generally regarded their installation in the church gallery as of divine right, and bitterly resented the advent of organs and harmoniums when they were introduced. The tradition lasted well into the nineteenth century, and surely not all the gallery choirs can have been bad. It is to this tradition that we owe the carol *Rejoice and be merry* (page 80), which comes from Dorset, and was found in an old gallery book there. Moreover, it was this tradition which kept alive the old carols and saved them for future generations.

Other traditions were kept up, too. In 1788 Parson Woodforde wrote: '. . . This being Christmas Eve I had my parlour windows dressed as usual with hulverboughs [holly] well seeded with red berries, and likewise in the kitchen.' He also took to lighting a large wax candle for about an hour on the afternoon of Christmas Day, and made the same candle last until 1800. A severe winter, as in 1796, might make Christmas a little less bright. 'We were obliged to have hulver branches without berries to dress up our windows etc. against Christmas, the weather having been so severe all this month that the poor birds have entirely already stript the bushes.' But the Christmas cheer was still there, and every year Parson Woodforde feasted the poor and elderly of his parish, until their numbers began to thin and shortly after the turn of the century he too expired.

The important thing was that the carol had been kept alive into the nineteenth century. A correspondent for the *Gentleman's Magazine* for 1811 told how he was awakened on Christmas Day in the North Riding of Yorkshire by a group of carol singers, and Washington Irving, also visiting Yorkshire, this time in 1820, was delighted at being serenaded by waits under his bedroom window. (Waits were groups of singers, or players and singers, often maintained by town councils to perform on special occasions. They developed from the night guards on the town gates, and survived into the eighteenth century, and even later in rural areas such as North Yorkshire.) By then it was almost too late in the estimation of some people to save the carol, but the tide had in fact turned, and 1822 saw the publication of the first modern collection of traditional carols.

The eighteenth century kept the carol alive, but it also contributed something of its own, and it is to this period that we owe such hymns as *Christians, awake* (page 44), as well as the words of *Hark! the herald angels sing* (page 57), and the tune of *Adeste fideles* or *O come, all ye faithful* (page 72).

It has often been said that Trad. and Anon. were the most prolific and gifted musician and lyricist that ever lived. On more than one occasion, however, they have simply been a cover for rather dubious musical ancestry. Without them our Christmas music would be immeasurably the poorer. Handed down from generation to generation in an age before recordings were possible, their survival has been little short of miraculous.

Luckily, interest in carols began early enough in the nineteenth century for much to be saved, and several collections were published, among them those of William Sandys, Bramley and Stainer, and W. H. Husk.

Thanks to the devotion of men like Cecil Sharp, who collected *The holly and the ivy* (page 94), and Ralph Vaughan Williams, who collected *The Sussex Carol*, the process was carried on into the present century.

One of the streams of tradition by which the carol survived has already been mentioned, namely the church choir, and Thomas Hardy's account in *Under the Greenwood Tree* rightly belongs here, since he was looking back into an earlier era at the time when he was writing.

> *Old William Dewy, with the violincello, played the bass; his grandson Dick the treble violin; and Reuben and Michael Mail the tenor and second violins respectively. The singers consisted of four men and seven boys, upon whom devolved the task of carrying and attending to the lanterns, and holding the books open for the players. Directly music was*

> *the theme, old William ever and instinctively came to the front.*

Such a band continued in use in many a church until well into the last century, and a photograph of the choir and band of Clewer Parish Church, Windsor, taken in 1879, shows exactly this combination. There was strong competition, however, on the one hand from wind instruments, and on the other from organs and harmoniums.

> 'Times have changed from the times they used to be,' said Mail, regarding nobody can tell what interesting old panoramas with an inward eye, and letting his outward glance rest on the ground, because it was as convenient a position as any. 'People don't care much about us now! I've been thinking; we must be almost the last left in the county of the old string players. Barrel-organs, and they next door to 'em that you blow wi' your foot, have come in terribly of late years.'
> 'More's the pity,' replied another. 'Time was – long and merry ago now! – when not one of the varmits was to be heard of; but it served some of the choirs right. They should have stuck to strings as we did, and keep out clar'nets, and done away with serpents. If you'd thrive in musical religion, stick to strings, says I.'

Finally the singers get down to their business of the evening:

> Then passed forth into the quiet night an ancient and well-worn hymn, embodying Christianity in words peculiarly befitting the simple and honest hearts of the quaint characters who sang them so earnestly.

> Remember Adam's fall,
> O thou man:
> Remember Adam's fall
> From Heaven to Hell.
> Remember Adam's fall;
> How he hath condemn'd all
> In Hell perpetual
> Therefore to dwell.

If we regard Hardy's characters as being representative of the main-stream of the Church of England at this time, then it was a side stream – though a very powerful one – that helped the restoration of the fortunes of the carol, for the growth of the Oxford Movement encouraged renewed interest in Church music, born of a desire to restore to worship some of its former dignity and splendour.

The carol may effortlessly bridge the centuries, since a hymn of the seventh century could be translated in the nineteenth, and set to music harmonized in the late sixteenth or early seventeenth, though the tune itself might be much older in origin. *A great and mighty wonder* (page 30) is one carol which follows this pattern.

Another carol which has been amalgamated from the traditions of succeeding centuries is one of the most famous of all, *Hark! the herald angels sing* (page 57). The music was adapted by W. H. Cummings (1831–1915) from a chorus by Mendelssohn. The composer thought that the music was really 'soldier-like and buxom', and suited to 'something gay and popular' rather than sacred. However, Cummings, who had sung as a choirboy under Mendelssohn in London, took a verse by C. Wesley of 1743, a second by T. Whitefield of 1753, and a third by M. Madan of 1760, to give us one of the best known of all carols.

Probably the most moving of all Victorian creations is *Once in royal David's city* (page 77). This carol-hymn is most associated with the opening of the service of nine lessons and carols from King's College Cambridge on Christmas Eve which, for many people all over the world, has come to symbolize Christmas itself and signifies the moment when the festival truly begins. A lone treble voice starts, then the choir joins in, and finally the entire congregation, as the hymn gathers up the whole of mankind in Jesus Christ's redemptive mission.

By this time the English-speaking world across the Atlantic was beginning to make its own contribution to the Christmas carol. Because the men and women who left England in the seventeenth century to settle in America were usually dissenters, they rarely took with them anything that was redolent of the great medieval tradition in Church music. Even so, we are grateful to their tradition as it developed on its own soil for some beautiful carols, amongst which are *Away in a manger* (page 38) and *We three kings* (page 108).

Apart from liturgical music and other anthems which are not carols, there is surprisingly little other Christmas music as such. Two of the most obvious works which spring to mind immediately are the pastoral symphonies from Handel's *Messiah* and Bach's *Christmas Oratorio*. In both these examples the drone-like effect of the bass is used to imitate the pipes of the shepherds out in the fields. There is also a Vivaldi concerto marked '*per il santissimo natale*', and Alessandro Scarlatti wrote a Christmas cantata, as did several lesser masters of the Baroque.

Carols have been a point of departure for organ music by Bach – choral preludes on *In dulci jubilo*, – and Brahms – on *Es ist ein' Ros' entsprungen* – and in more recent times for a Christmas fantasia by Vaughan Williams. In the present century, also, Gian Carlo Menotti has written a Christmas opera *Amahl and the Night Visitors*, and Benjamin Britten a delightful miniature for harp and boys' voices, *A Ceremony of Carols*, which draws heavily on Church and medieval tradition once more.

One could do little better than close this outline of the music of Christmas and the carol with some words of Ralph Vaughan Williams from his preface to the Oxford Book of Carols, first published in 1928. At the time of his death some thirty years later he was about to undertake a revision of this book, but what he wrote in 1929 is just as true today:

> *It is a thrilling history, full of significance. Something transparently pure and truthful, clean and merry as the sunshine, has been recovered from under the crust of artificiality which had hidden it. The English-speaking peoples are now getting back what once belonged to them, both in poetry and music, through the researches of a few scholars and through the conservatism of old village folk and the work of a few musicians who could recognize beauty when they saw it. The carol is established again . . .*

A CHILD THIS DAY IS BORN

English traditional carol

1. A child this day is born, a child of high re-nown;
2. These ti-dings shep-herds heard whilst watch-ing o'er their fold;
3. Then was there with the an-gel an host in-con-tin-ent

most wor-thy of a scep-tre, a scep-tre and a crown.
'twas by an an-gel un-to them that night re-vealed and told.
of heav-en-ly bright sold-iers, all from the high-est sent.

4. They praised the Lord our God,
And our celestial King:
All glory be in paradise
This heav'nly host do sing.

5. All glory be to God,
That sitteth still on high,
With praises and with triumph great,
And joyful melody.

Optional Descant

No-well, No-well, No-well sing all we may,

No-well, No-well, No-well, No-well sing all we may,

be-cause the King of ..all kings was born up-on this day.

be-cause the King of all kings was born up-on this day.

A GREAT AND MIGHTY WONDER

Words by ST GERMANUS
Translated by J. M. NEALE

Old German tune
Harmonised by M. PRAETORIUS

1. A great and migh-ty won-der, a full and ho-ly cure!
The Vir-gin bears the In-fant with vir-gin hon-our pure!

Descant for final refrain

Re-peat the hymn a-gain!

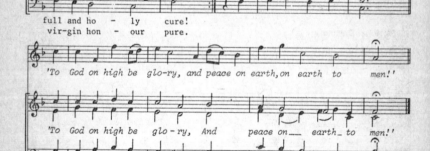

full and ho-ly cure! Re-peat the hymn a-gain!
vir-gin hon-our pure.

full and ho-ly cure!
vir-gin hon-our pure.

'To God on high be glo-ry, and peace on earth, on earth to men!'

'To God on high be glo-ry, And peace on earth to men!'

earth to men!'

2. The word becomes incarnate
And yet remains on high!
And cherubim sing anthems
To shepherds from the sky.
Repeat the hymn again! etc.

3. While thus they sing your Monarch,
Those bright angelic bands,
Rejoice, ye vales and mountains,
Ye oceans clap your hands.
Repeat the hymn again! etc.

4. Since all he comes to ransom,
By all be he adored,
The Infant born in Bethl'em
The Saviour and the Lord.
Repeat the hymn again! etc.

5. And idol forms shall perish,
And error shall decay,
And Christ shall wield his sceptre,
Our Lord and God for ay.
Repeat the hymn again! etc.

30

A MERRY CHRISTMAS

(WE WISH YOU A MERRY CHRISTMAS)

West country traditional carol

1. We wish you a mer-ry Christ-mas, we wish you a mer-ry
2. Now bring us some fig-gy pud-ding, now bring us some fig-gy
3. For we all like fig-gy pud-ding, for we all like fig-gy
4. And we won't go till we've got some, and we won't go till we've

Christ-mas, we wish you a mer-ry Christ-mas and a hap-py New Year.
pud-ding, now bring us some fig-gy pud-ding and bring some out here.
pud-ding, for we all like fig-gy pud-ding so bring some out here.
got some, and we won't go till we've got some so bring some out here.

Good tid-ings I bring to you and your kin; we

wish you a mer-ry Christ-mas and a hap-py New Year.

A VIRGIN MOST PURE

English traditional carol

1. A virgin most pure, as the prophets do tell, hath brought forth a baby, as it hath befell; to be our Redeemer from death, hell, and sin, which Adam's transgression had wrapped us in.

2. In Bethlehem Jewry a city there was, where Joseph and Mary together did pass, and there to be taxed with many one mo, for Caesar commanded the same should be so.

Aye, and therefore be

mer-ry; re-joice, and be you mer-ry; set sor-row a-

-side; Christ Je-sus our Sa-viour was born at this tide.

3. But when they had enter'd the city so fair,
   A number of people so mighty was there,
   That Joseph and Mary, whose substance was small,
   Could find in the inn there no lodging at all.
   Aye, and therefore, etc.

4. Then they were constrain'd in a stable to lie,
   Where horses and asses they us'd for to tie;
   Their lodging so simple they took it no scorn,
   But against the next morning our Saviour was born.
   Aye, and therefore, etc.

5. The King of all kings to this world being brought,
   Small store of fine linen to wrap him was sought;
   And when she had swaddled her young Son so sweet,
   Within an ox-manger she laid him to sleep.
   Aye, and therefore, etc.

6. Then God sent an angel from heaven so high,
   To certain poor shepherds in fields where they lie,
   And bade them no longer in sorrow to stay,
   Because that our Saviour was born on this day.
   Aye, and therefore, etc.

7. Then presently after the shepherds did spy
   A number of angels that stood in the sky;
   They joyfully talked and sweetly did sing,
   'To God be all glory our heavenly King.'
   Aye, and therefore, etc.

Verses with an asterisk may be omitted.

33

ANGELS FROM THE REALMS

Words by J. MONTGOMERY

Old French tune

1. An-gels, from the realms _ of glo-ry, wing your flight o'er all the earth;
2. Shep-herds in the field _ a-bi-ding, watch-ing o'er your flocks by night,

ye who sang cre - a-tion's sto-ry_ now pro-claim Mes - si - ah's birth:
God with man is_ now re-si-ding; yon-der shines the_ in-fant light:

Glo - - - - - - - - ri-a

in _ ex - cel-sis De - o. _ Glo - - -

- - - - ri-a in _ ex - cel-sis De - - o.

34

3. Sages, leave your contemplations;
   Brighter visions beam afar;
   Seek the great desire of nations;
   Ye have seen his natal star:
   Gloria in excelsis Deo.

4. Saints before the altar bending,
   Watching long in hope and fear,
   Suddenly the Lord, descending,
   In his temple shall appear:
   Gloria in excelsis Deo.

5. Though an infant now we view him,
   He shall fill his father's throne,
   Gather all the nations to him;
   Every knee shall then bow down:
   Gloria in excelsis Deo.

ALL MY HEART

Words by PAULUS GERHARDT
Translated by
CATHERINE WINKWORTH

Tune by
JOHANN GEORG EBELING

1. All my heart this night re - joi - ces as I
2. Hark! a voice from yon - der man - ger, soft and

1. All my heart
2. Hark! a voice

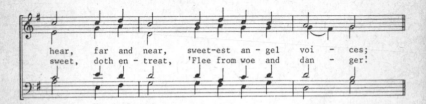

hear, far and near, sweet-est an - gel voi - ces;
sweet, doth en - treat, 'Flee from woe and dan - ger!

'Christ is born' their choirs are sing-ing till the
breth - ren, come! from all doth grieve you, you are

Christ is born
breth-ren, come!

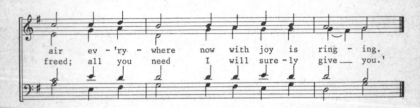

air ev - 'ry - where now with joy is ring - ing.
freed; all you need I will sure - ly give you.'

3. Come, then, let us hasten yonder!
   Here let all, great and small,
   Kneel in awe and wonder!
   Love him who with love is yearning!
   Hail the star that from far
   Bright with hope is burning!

4. Thee, dear Lord, with heed I'll cherish,
   Live to thee, and with thee,
   Dying, shall not perish;
   But shall dwell with thee for ever,
   Far on high, in the joy
   That can alter never.

36

AS WITH GLADNESS

Words by
W. CHATTERTON DIX

Abridged from a chorale
by C. KOCHER

1. As with gladness men of old did the guiding star behold,
as with joy they hailed its light, leading onward, beaming bright,
so, most gracious God, may we evermore be led to thee.

2. As with joyful steps they sped,
To that lowly manger-bed,
There to bend the knee before
Him whom heaven and earth adore,
So may we with willing feet
Ever seek thy mercy-seat.

3. As they offered gifts most rare
At that manger rude and bare,
So may we with holy joy,
Pure, and free from sin's alloy,
All our costliest treasures bring,
Christ, to thee our heavenly King.

4. Holy Jesu, every day
Keep us in the narrow way;
And, when earthly things are past,
Bring our ransomed souls at last
Where they need no star to guide,
Where no clouds thy glory hide.

5. In the heav'nly country bright
Need they no created light;
Thou its light, its joy, its crown,
Thou its sun which goes not down:
There for ever may we sing
Alleluyas to our King.

AWAY IN A MANGER

Words anon.

Tune by W. J. KIRKPATRICK

1. A - way in a __ man - ger, no __ crib for a bed,
2. The cat - tle are __ low - ing, the __ ba - by a - wakes,
3. Be near me, Lord Je - sus; I __ ask thee to stay

the __ lit - tle Lord Je - sus laid __ down his sweet head.
but __ lit - tle Lord Je - sus no __ cry - ing he makes.
close by me for e - ver, and __ love me, I pray.

The stars in the __ bright sky looked down where he lay,
I love thee, Lord Je - sus! look __ down from the sky,
Bless all the dear __ chil - dren in __ thy ten - der care,

the __ lit - tle Lord Je - sus a - sleep on the __ hay.
and __ stay by my side un - til __ morn - ing is __ nigh.
and __ fit us for hea - ven, to __ live with thee __ there.

BETHLEHEM OF NOBLEST CITIES

Words by PRUDENTIUS
Translated by
EDWARD CASSWALL

Adapted from a fourteenth-century
German tune

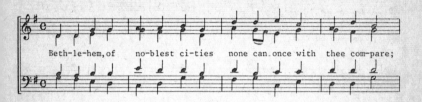

Beth-le-hem, of no-blest ci-ties none can once with thee com-pare;

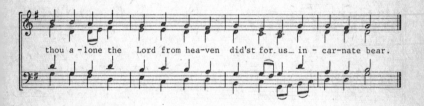

thou a -lone the Lord from hea-ven did'st for us_ in - car-nate bear.

2. Fairer than the sun at morning
   Was the star that told his birth;
   To the lands their God announcing,
   His beneath a form of earth.

3. By its lambent beauty guided
   See the eastern kings appear;
   See them bend their gifts to offer.
   Gifts of incense, gold and myrrh.

4. Solemn things of mystic meaning:
   Incense doth the God disclose,
   Gold a royal child proclaimeth,
   Myrrh a future tomb foreshows.

5. Holy Jesu, in thy brightness
   To the gentile world displayed,
   With the Father and the Spirit
   Endless praise to thee be paid.

BLESSED BE THAT MAID

Words by G. R. WOODWARD

English traditional tune

Bles-sed be that maid Ma-rie; born he was of her bo-dy; ve-ry God ere time be-gan, born in time the Son of Man. E - ya! Je-sus ho-di-e na-tus est de vir-gi-ne.

2. In a manger of an ass
   Jesu lay and lullèd was;
   Born to die upon the tree
   Pro peccante homine.
       Eya! etc.

3. Sweet and blissful was the song
   Chanted of the angel throng,
   'Peace on earth,' Alleluya.
   In excelsis gloria.
       Eya! etc.

4. Fare three kings from far-off land,
   Incense, gold and myrrh in hand;
   In Bethlem the Babe they see,
   Stellæ ducti lumine.
       Eya! etc.

5. Make we merry on this fest,
   In quo Christus natus est;
   On this Child I pray you call
   To assoil and save us all.
       Eya! etc.

BOAR'S HEAD CAROL

(*THE BOAR'S HEAD IN HAND BEAR I*)

English traditional carol

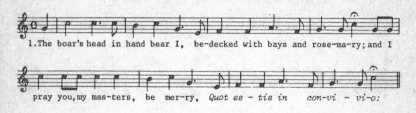

1. The boar's head in hand bear I, be-decked with bays and rose-ma-ry; and I

pray you, my mas-ters, be mer-ry, *Quot es – tis in con-vi – vi-o:*

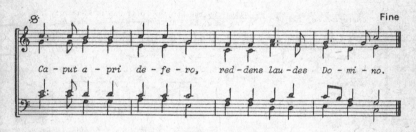

Ca – put a – pri de – fe – ro, red-dens lau-des Do – mi – no. Fine

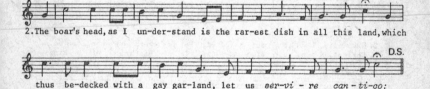

2. The boar's head, as I un-der-stand is the rar-est dish in all this land, which

thus be-decked with a gay gar-land, let us *ser-vi – re can-ti-co:* D.S.

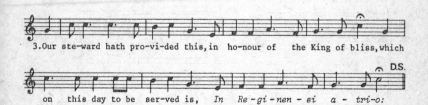

3. Our ste-ward hath pro-vi-ded this, in ho-nour of the King of bliss, which

on this day to be ser-ved is, *In Re-gi-nen-si a – tri-o:* D.S.

CHRIST WAS BORN

Words by J. M. NEALE

Old German tune

42

5. Night of sad-ness, morn of glad-ness e - ver-more: e - ver, e - ver:

Af - ter ma - ny trou-bles sore,

Ah,
Ah,

morn of glad-ness e - ver-more and

Ah,

6. Mid-night scarce-ly past and o - ver, draw-ing to this

e-ver-more.

Ah.
Ah.

Ah.

ho - ly morn:

Fine

ve - ry ear-ly, ve - ry ear-ly Christ was born.

7. Sing out with bliss, his name is this: _____ Em-man-u-

D.S.

-el: _____ as was fore-told in days of old by Ga-bri-el.

43

CHRISTIANS, AWAKE

Words by J. BYROM   Tune by JOHN WAINWRIGHT

1. Chris-tians, a - wake, sa - lute the hap-py morn where - on the
Sa-viour of man - kind was born; rise to a - dore the
mys-te - ry of love, which hosts of an-gels chan-ted from a -
-bove; with them the joy - ful ti -dings first be - gun
of God in - car - nate and the Vir - gin's Son.

2. Then to the watchful shepherds it was told,
   Who heard th' angelic herald's voice, 'Behold
   I bring you tidings of a Saviour's birth
   To you and all the nations upon earth:
   This day hath God fulfilled his promised word,
   This day is born a Saviour, Christ the Lord.'

3. He spake: and straightway the celestial choir
   In hymns of joy, unknown before, conspire:
   The praises of redeeming love they sang,
   And heav'ns whole orb with alleluyas rang:
   God's highest glory was their anthem still,
   Peace upon earth, and unto men goodwill.

4. To Bethl'em straight th' enlightened shepherds ran,
   To see the wonder God had wrought for man,
   And found, with Joseph and the blessed Maid,
   Her Son, the Saviour, in a manger laid:
   Then to their flocks, still praising God, return,
   And their glad hearts with holy rapture burn.

5. O may we keep and ponder in our mind
   God's wondrous love in saving lost mankind:
   Trace we the Babe, who hath retrieved our loss,
   From his poor manger to his bitter cross;
   Tread in his steps, assisted by his grace,
   Till man's first heav'nly state again takes place.

6. Then may we hope, th' angelic thrones among,
   To sing, redeemed, a glad triumphal song;
   He that was born upon this joyful day,
   Around us all his glory shall display;
   Saved by his love, incessant shall we sing
   Eternal praise to heaven's almighty King.

COME LEAVE YOUR SHEEP

(*QUITTEZ, PASTEURS*)

English words by JOHN RUTTER

French traditional carol

1. Come leave your sheep, your ewes with lambs a-feeding, O shep-herds, hear our mes-sage of good cheer; no long-er weep; the an-gel-ti-dings heed-ing, to Beth-lem haste a-way! Our Lord, our Lord, Our Lord, our Lord, our Lord is born this hap-py day. Lord, our Lord Our Lord, our Lord, our Lord is born this hap-py day.

1. *Quit-tez, pas-teurs, vos bre-bis, vos hou-let-tes, vo-tre ha-meau et le soin du trou-peau; chan-gez vos pleurs en u-ne joie par-fai-te; al-lez tous a-dor-er un Dieu, un Dieu, Un Dieu, un Dieu, un Dieu qui vient vous con-so-ler. Dieu, un Dieu, Un Dieu, un Dieu, un Dieu qui vient vous con-so-ler.*

2. He lieth there within a lowly manger;
   An infant poor he languisheth full sore.
   God's loving care hath saved us from all danger
   And brought us to his fold;
   Now own, now own
   His faithful love revealed of old.
   Now own, now own
   His faithful love revealed of old.

3. Ye sages three arrayed in royal splendour,
   Your homage pay; a King is born this day.
   The star ye see its radiance must surrender
   Before our sun most bright;
   Your gifts, your gifts,
   Your gifts are precious in his sight.
   Your gifts, your gifts,
   Your gifts are precious in his sight.

4. Come Holy Ghost, of blessings source eternal,
   Our souls inspire with thy celestial fire;
   The heav'nly host praise Christ the Lord supernal
   And sing the peace on earth
   God gives, God gives,
   God gives us by his holy birth.
   God gives, God gives,
   God gives us by his holy birth.

2. *Vous leverez couche dans une etable*
   Comme un enfant nu, pauvre, languissant;
   Reconnaissez son amour ineffable
   Pour nous venir chercher
   Il est, il est,
   Il est le fidèle berger!
   Il est, il est,
   Il est le fidèle berger!

3. *Rois d'Orient l'étoile vous eclaire;*
   A ce grand roi rendez hommage et foi.
   L'astre brillant vous mene a la lumiere
   De ce soleil naissant;
   Offrez, offrez,
   Offrez l'or, la myrrhe et l'encens.
   Offrez, offrez,
   Offrez l'or, la myrrhe et l'encens.

4. *Esprit divin à qui tout est possible*
   Percez nos coeurs de vos douces ardeurs;
   Notre destin par vous devient paisible;
   Dieu prétend nous donner
   Le ciel, le ciel,
   Le ciel en venant s'incarner.
   Le ciel, le ciel,
   Le ciel en venant s'incarner.

COME ALL YOU WORTHY GENTLEMEN

Words collected by CECIL SHARP

Old English tune

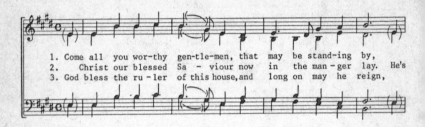

1. Come all you wor-thy gen-tle-men, that may be stand-ing by,
2. Christ our blessed Sa - viour now in the man - ger lay. He's
3. God bless the ru - ler of this house, and long on may he reign,

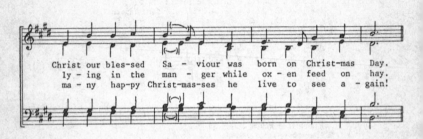

Christ our bles-sed Sa - viour was born on Christ-mas Day.
ly - ing in the man - ger while ox - en feed on hay.
ma - ny hap-py Christ-mas-ses he live to see a - gain!

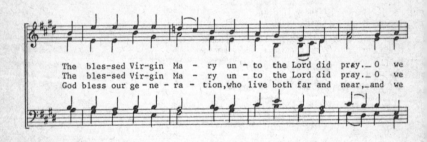

The bles-sed Vir-gin Ma - ry un - to the Lord did pray._ O we
The bles-sed Vir-gin Ma - ry un - to the Lord did pray._ O we
God bless our ge - ne - ra - tion, who live both far and near,_and we

wish _ you the com - fort and ti - dings of joy!
wish _ you the com - fort and ti - dings of joy!
wish _ them a hap - py, a hap - py New Year.

COVENTRY CAROL

(*LULLY, LULLA, THOU LITTLE TINY CHILD*)

Words fifteenth century

Sixteenth-century tune

Lul-ly, lul-la, thou lit-tle ti-ny child, by by, lul-ly lul - lay.

1. O sis-ters how may we do for to pre-serve this day this poor young-ling, for whom we do sing, by by, lul-ly lul - lay?
2. He - rod, the in his rag-ing, char-ged he hath this day his men of might, in his own sight, all young chil-dren to slay.
3. That woe is poor child for thee! and ev-er morn and day, for thy part-ing nei-ther say nor sing by by, lul-ly lul - lay!

(After 3rd verse, repeat refrain) D.S.

DECK THE HALL

Welsh traditional carol

1. Deck the hall with boughs of hol-ly,
2. See the flow-ing bowl be-fore us,
3. Fast a-way the old year passes,

Fa la la la la, fa la la la,

'Tis the sea-son to be jol-ly,
Strike the harp and join the cho-rus,
Hail the new, ye lads and las-sies,

Fa la la la la, fa la la la la.

Fill the mead cup, drain the bar-rel,
Fol-low me in mer-ry mea-sure,
Laugh-ing, quaffing all to-ge-ther,

Fa la la la la, fa la la la,

Fill the mead cup, drain the bar-rel,
Fol-low me in mer-ry mea-sure,
Laugh-ing, quaffing all to-ge-ther,

Fa   fa la la la la,

Troll the an-cient Christ-mas ca-rol,
While I sing of beau-ty's trea-sure,
Heed-less of the wind and wea-ther

Fa la la la la, fa la la la la.
(fa)

Fa la la,

DING DONG! MERRILY ON HIGH

Words by G. R. WOODWARD   Sixteenth-century French tune

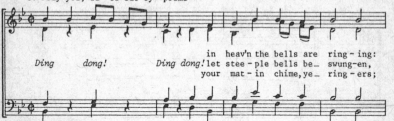

GABRIEL'S MESSAGE

(THE ANGEL GABRIEL FROM HEAVEN CAME)

Words by S. BARING-GOULD

Basque carol

1. The an - gel Ga - bri-el from hea - ven came, his wings as drift - ed snow, his eyes ___ as flame; 'All hail,' said he, 'thou low - ly mai - den Ma - ry, ___ high-ly fa-vour'd la - dy, Glo - ri - a!

2. 'For known a bless-ed mo - ther thou shalt be, all ge - ne - ra - tions laud and ho - nour thee, ___ thy Son shall be Em - ma - nu - el, by seers fore-told, ___

3. Then gen - tle Ma - ry meek - ly bowed her head, 'to me be as it pleas - eth God,' she said, ___ 'My soul shall laud and mag - ni - fy his ho - ly name.' ___

4. Of her, Em - ma - nu - el, the Christ was born in Beth - le - hem, all on a Christ - mas morn, ___ and Chris - tian folk throughout the world will ev - er say: ___

Most

Ah,

Glo - ri - a!

52

GOD REST YOU MERRY

English traditional carol

1. God rest you mer-ry, gen-tle-men, let no-thing you dis-may,
for Je-sus Christ our Sa-viour was born up-on this day,
to save us all from Sa-tan's power when we were gone a-stray:
O— ti-dings of com-fort and joy, com-fort and joy,— O— ti-dings of com-fort and— joy.

2. From God our heav'nly Fa-ther a bless-ed an-gel came,
and un-to cer-tain shep-herds brought ti-dings of the same,
how that in Beth-le-hem was born the Son of God by name:

3. The shepherds at those tidings
Rejoiced much in mind,
And left their flocks a-feeding,
In tempest, storm and wind,
And went to Bethlehem straightway
This blessed babe to find:
O tidings of comfort and joy.

4. But when to Bethlehem they came,
Whereat this infant lay,
They found him in a manger,
Where oxen feed on hay;
His mother Mary kneeling,
Unto the Lord did pray:
O tidings of comfort and joy.

5. Now to the Lord sing praises,
All you within this place,
And with true love and brotherhood
Each other now embrace;
This holy tide of Christmas
All others doth deface:
O tidings of comfort and joy.

GOOD KING WENCESLAS

Words by J. M. NEALE   Tune from *Piae Cantiones*

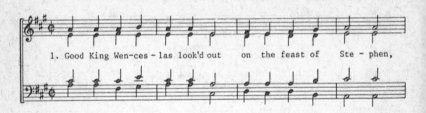

1. Good King Wen-ces-las look'd out on the feast of Ste - phen,

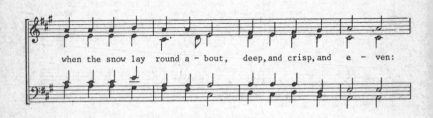

when the snow lay round a - bout, deep, and crisp, and e - ven:

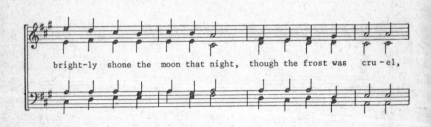

bright-ly shone the moon that night, though the frost was cru -el,

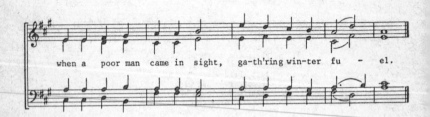

when a poor man came in sight, ga-th'ring win-ter fu - el.

2. 'Hither, page, and stand by me,
   If thou know'st it, telling,
   Yonder peasant, who is he?
   Where and what his dwelling?'
   'Sire, he lives a good league hence,
   Underneath the mountain;
   Right against the forest fence,
   By St. Agnes' fountain.'

3. 'Bring me flesh, and bring me wine,
   Bring me pine logs hither;
   Thou and I will see him dine,
   When we bear them thither.'
   Page and monarch forth they went,
   Forth they went together;
   Through the rude wind's wild lament,
   And the bitter weather.

4. 'Sire, the night is darker now,
   And the wind blows stronger;
   Fails my heart, I know not how,
   I can go no longer.'
   'Mark my footsteps, good my page!
   Tread thou in them boldly:
   Thou shalt find the winter's rage
   Freeze thy blood less coldly.'

5. In his master's steps he trod,
   Where the snow lay dinted;
   Heat was in the very sod
   Which the saint had printed.
   Therefore, Christian men, be sure,
   Wealth or rank possessing,
   Ye who now will bless the poor,
   Shall yourselves find blessing.

If sung in unison with accompaniment, the following arrangement is suggested.

Verse 1	*All singers*
Verse 2	*Men only lines 1 - 4, women or boys lines 5 - 8*
Verse 3	*Men only lines 1 - 4, all singers lines 5 - 8*
Verse 4	*Women or boys lines 1 - 4, men 5 - 8*
Verse 5	*All singers*

HAIL, BLESSED VIRGIN MARY

Words by G. R. WOODWARD

Italian carol
Arranged by CHARLES WOOD

1. Hail! bless-ed Vir-gin Ma - ry! For so when he did meet thee, spake migh-ty Ga-bri-el, and thus we greet thee. Come weal, come woe, our hymn shall nev-er va-ry. Hail! bless-ed Vir-gin Ma - ry! Hail! bless-ed Vir-gin Ma - ry!

2. A - ve, a - ve Ma - ri - a! To glad-den priest and peo - ple, the an - ge-lus shall ring from ev-'ry stee - ple, to sound his vir-gin birth, Al - le-lu-y - a! A - ve, a - ve Ma-ri - a! A - ve, a - ve Ma-ri - a!

3. Arch - an-gels chant O - san - na, And ho-ly, ho-ly, ho - ly, be - fore the in-fant born of thee, thou low - ly, aye mai - den child of Jo - a - chim and An - na; Arch-an-gels chant O - san - na. Arch - an-gels chant O - san - na.

HARK! THE HERALD ANGELS SING

Words by C. WESLEY,
T. WHITEFIELD, M. MADAN
and others

Tune by MENDELSSOHN
(Slightly adapted)

1. Hark! the he-rald an-gels sing_ glo-ry to the new-born King;
2. Christ, by high-est heav'n a-dored, Christ, the e-ver-last-ing Lord,
3. Hail the heav'nborn Prince of peace! hail the Son of right-eous-ness!

peace on earth and mer-cy mild,_ God and sin-ners re-con-ciled:
late in time be-hold him come_ off-spring of a vir-gin's womb:
light and life to all he brings, ris'n with heal-ing in his wings;

joy-ful all ye na-tions rise,_ join the tri-umph of the skies,
veiled in flesh the God-head see,_ hail th'in-car-nate De-i-ty!
mild he lays his glo-ry by, _ born that man no more may die,_

with th'an-gel-ic host pro-claim, Christ is_ born in Beth-le-hem.
pleased as man with man to dwell, Je-sus,_ our Em-ma-nu-el.
born to raise the sons of earth, born to_ give them se-cond birth.

Hark! the he-rald an-gels sing glo-ry_ to the new-born King.

HE IS BORN, THE DIVINE CHRIST-CHILD

(*IL EST NE*)

English words by
DAVID WILLCOCKS

French traditional carol

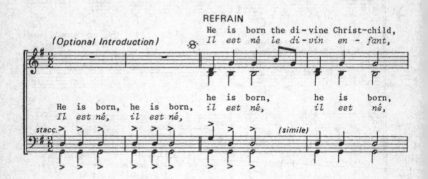

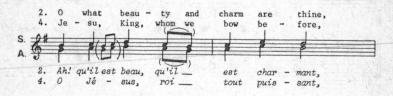

HERE WE COME A-WASSAILING

English traditional carol

1. Here we come a-was-sail-ing a-mong the leaves so green,
2. Our was-sail cup is made of the rose-ma-ry tree,

— here we come a-wan-der-ing, so fair to be
and so is your beer of the best bar-

seen: Love and joy come to you and to you your was-sail
-ley:

too, and God bless you, and send you a hap-py New

Year, and God send you a hap-py New Year.

3. We are not daily beggars
   That beg from door to door,
   But we are neighbours' children
   Whom you have seen before:

4. Call up the butler of this house,
   Put on his golden ring;
   Let him bring us up a glass of beer,
   And better shall we sing:

5. We've got a little purse
   Of stretching leather skin;
   We want a little of your money
   To line it well within:

6. Bring us out a table,
   And spread it with a cloth;
   Bring us out a mouldy cheese,
   And some of your Christmas loaf:

7. God bless the master of this house,
   Likewise the mistress too;
   And all the little children
   That round the table go:

8. Good Master and good Mistress,
   While you're sitting by the fire,
   Pray think of us poor children
   That's wandered in the mire:

HOW FAR IS IT TO BETHLEHEM?

Words by
FRANCIS CHESTERTON

English traditional tune

IN DULCI JUBILO

English translation by
R. L. PEARSALL

Old German tune
Arranged by R. L. PEARSALL

1. *In dul-ci ju-bi-lo* ___ let us our hom-age shew; ___
2. *O Je-su, par-vu-le,* ___ I yearn for thee al-way, ___

our heart's joy re-cli-neth *in prae-se-pi-o,* ___ and
hear me, I be-seech thee, *O puer op-ti-me,* ___ my

like a bright star shi-neth, *ma-tris in gre-mi-o.* ___
pray-er let it reach thee, *O prin-ceps glo-ri-ae.* ___

Al-pha es et O! ___ *Al-pha es et O!* ___
Tra-he me post te! ___ *Tra-he me post te!* ___

3. *O patris caritas!*
   O nati lenitas!
   Deeply were we stainèd
   Per nostra crimina;
   But thou hast for us gainèd
   Coelorum gaudia.
   O that we were there,
   O that we were there!

4. *Ubi sunt gaudia,*
   If that they be not there?
   There are angels singing
   Nova cantica,
   There the bells are ringing
   In regis curia:
   O that we were there,
   O that we were there!

I SAW THREE SHIPS

English traditional carol

1. I saw three ships come sail - ing in,
3. Our sa - viour Christ and his la - dy,
5. O, they sailed in to Beth - le - hem,
7. And all the an gels in heav'n shall sing,

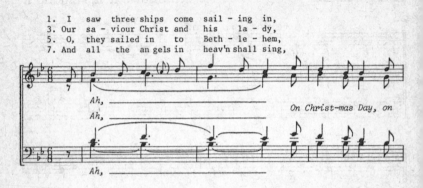

I saw three ships come sail - ing in,
our sa - viour Christ and his la - dy,
O, they sailed in to Beth - le - hem,
and all the an gels in heav'n shall sing,

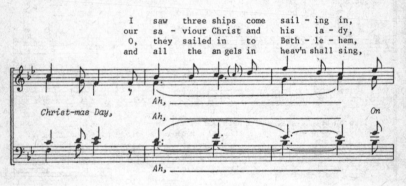

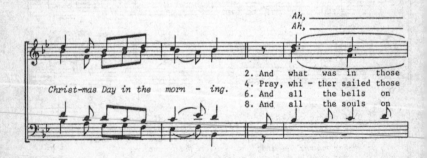

2. And what was in those
4. Pray, whi - ther sailed those
6. And all the bells on
8. And all the souls on

ships all three?
ships all three?
earth shall ring, *On Christ-mas Day, on Christ-mas Day,* and
earth shall sing, pray,
and
and

Ah,
Ah,

what was in those ships all three?
whi-ther sailed those ships all three?
all the bells on earth shall ring, *On Christ-mas Day in the morn-ing.*
all the souls on earth shall sing,

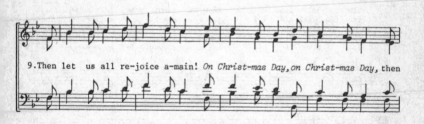

9.Then let us all re-joice a-main! *On Christ-mas Day, on Christ-mas Day,* then

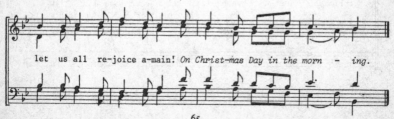

let us all re-joice a-main! *On Christ-mas Day in the morn - ing.*

IN THE BLEAK MID-WINTER

Words by
CHRISTINA ROSSETTI

Tune by GUSTAV HOLST

1. In the bleak mid - win - ter fros - ty wind made moan,
2. Our God, heav'n can - not hold him nor earth sus - tain;
3. E-nough for him, whom che-ru - bim wor-ship night and day, a
4. An - gels and arch - an - gels may have ga-thered there,
5. What can I give him, poor as I am?

earth stood hard as i - ron, wa - ter like a stone;
heav'n and earth shall flee a-way when he comes to reign:
breast - ful of milk, and a man-ger - ful of hay; e-
che - ru - bim and se - ra-phim thronged the air: but
if I were a shep - herd I would bring a lamb;

snow had fal - len, snow on snow, snow on snow,
in the bleak mid - win - ter a sta-ble-place suf - ficed the
-nough for him, whom an - gels fall down be - fore, the
on - ly his mo - ther in her maid - en bliss
if I were a wise man I would do my part; yet

in the bleak mid - win - ter, long a - go.
Lord God Al - migh - ty Je - sus Christ.
ox and ass and ca - mel which a - dore.
wor-shipped the be - lo - ved with a kiss.
what I can I give him — give my heart.

INFANT HOLY, INFANT LOWLY

Translation by EDITH M. REED

Polish carol

1. In-fant ho-ly, in-fant low-ly, for his bed a cat-tle
2. Flocks were sleep-ing, shep-herds keep-ing vi-gil till the morn-ing

stall; ox-en low-ing, lit-tle know-ing Christ the Babe is Lord of
new, saw the glo-ry, heard the sto-ry, ti-dings of a gos-pel

all. Swift are wing-ing an-gels sing-ing, No-wells ring-ing, ti-dings
true. Thus re-joic-ing, free from sor-row, prai-ses voic-ing, greet the

bring-ing, Christ the Babe is Lord of all, Christ the Babe is Lord of all.
mor-row, Christ the Babe was born for you, Christ the Babe was born for you.

IT CAME UPON THE MIDNIGHT CLEAR

Words by H. SEARS

Traditional English tune
Adapted by
ARTHUR SULLIVAN

1. It came up-on the mid-night clear, that glo-rious song of old,
2. Still through the clo-ven skies they come, with peace-ful wings un-furled;

from an - gels bend-ing near the earth to touch their harps of gold:
and still their heav'n-ly mu - sic floats o'er all the wea - ry world;

'Peace on the earth, good - will to men, from heav'n's all-grac-ious King!'
a - bove its sad and low - ly plains they bend on ho-v'ring wing;

The world in so - lemn still-ness lay to hear the an - gels sing.
and ev - er o'er its Ba - bel sounds the bless-ed an - gels sing.

3. Yet with the woes of sin and strife
   The world has suffered long;
   Beneath the angel-strain have rolled
   Two thousand years of wrong;
   And man, at war with man, hears not
   The love-song which they bring:
   O hush the noise, ye men of strife,
   And hear the angels sing!

4. For lo! the days are hastening on,
   By prophet-bards foretold,
   When, with the ever-circling years,
   Comes round the age of gold;
   When peace shall over all the earth
   Its ancient splendours fling,
   And the whole world send back the song
   Which now the angels sing.

KING JESUS HATH A GARDEN

Translation by
G. R. WOODWARD

Dutch tune

1. King Je - sus hath a gar - den, full of di - vers
2. The li - ly, white in blos - som there, is Chas - ti -

flow'rs, where I go cull - ing po - sies gay, all times and
- ty: the vi - o - let, with sweet per - fume, Hu - mi - li -

hours. There naught is heard but Pa - ra - dise bird, harp, dul - ci - mer, lute,
- ty.

with cym - bal, with cym - bal, trump and tym - bal, and the ten - der, sooth - ing flute;

with cym - bal, with cym - bal, trump and tym - bal, and the ten - der, sooth - ing flute.

3. The bonny damask-rose is known as Patïence:
   The blithe and thrifty marygold, Obedïence.

   There naught is heard, etc.

4. The crown imperial bloometh too in yonder place,
   'Tis Charity, of stock divine, the flower of grace.

   There naught is heard, etc.

5. Yet, 'mid the brave, the bravest prize of all may claim
   The Star of Bethlem – **Jesus** – blessèd be his name!

   There naught is heard, etc.

6. Ah! Jesu Lord, my heal and weal, my bliss complete,
   Make thou my heart thy garden-plot, fair, trim and neat.
   That I may hear this musick clear:
   Harp, dulcimer, lute,
   With cymbal, trump and tymbal,
   And the tender, soothing flute.

O COME, ALL YE FAITHFUL

(*ADESTE FIDELES*)

Translated by F. OAKELEY,
W. T. BROOKE and others

Tune by J. F. WADE

God ___ in the high-est: *O come, let us a-dore him,*

born the King of an - gels:
- got -ten, not cre - a - ted: *O*   *O come, let us a - dore*   *him, O*
in ___ the ___ high - est:
now in flesh ap -pear - ing:

O come, let us a-dore him,   *O come, let us a -*

come, let us a - dore   him, O   come, let us   a -

-dore him,   a - dore him, Christ the Lord.

-dore ___ him, ___ Christ ___ the Lord.

O COME, O COME, EMMANUEL

Words eighteenth century

Fifteenth-century French tune

1. O come, O come, Emmanuel! Redeem thy captive Israel, that into exile drear is gone far from the face of God's dear Son. Rejoice! rejoice! Emmanuel shall come to thee, O Israel.

2. O come, thou Branch of Jesse! draw
The quarry from the lion's claw;
From the dread caverns of the grave,
From nether hell, thy people save.

   Rejoice! rejoice! Emmanuel
   Shall come to thee, O Israel.

   O come, O come, thou Dayspring bright!
   Pour on our souls thy healing light;
   Dispel the long night's ling'ring gloom,
   And pierce the shadows of the tomb.

   Rejoice! rejoice! Emmanuel
   Shall come to thee, O Israel.

4. O come, thou Lord of David's Key!
The royal door fling wide and free;
Safeguard for us the heav'nward road,
And bar the way to death's abode.

   Rejoice! rejoice! Emmanuel
   Shall come to thee, O Israel.

5. O come, O come, Adonai,
Who in thy glorious majesty
From that high mountain clothed with awe
Gavest thy folk the elder law.

   Rejoice! rejoice! Emmanuel
   Shall come to thee, O Israel.

O JESUS, SWEET CHILD

Words anon.

Tune by J. S. BACH

1.
2. O Je-sus, sweet Child, thou gen-tle and mild! Thy Fath—er's
3.

will— thou hast— ful-fill'd. Thou left—est heav—en—
ang— er hast— thou still'd, our guilt— thou bear—est—
glad— ness hast— thou fill'd. Thou cam—est down— from

for— our sake, and our— frail flesh— on thee— didst
in— our place and win—nest us— thy Fa— ther's
heav—en's height, to bring— us com—fort in— our

take.—
grace.— O Je-sus, sweet Child,— thou gen—tle and mild.
night.—

O LITTLE TOWN OF BETHLEHEM

Words by PHILLIPS BROOKS

English traditional carol

1. O lit-tle town of Beth-le-hem, how still we see thee lie!
2. O morn-ing stars, to-geth-er pro-claim the ho-ly birth,

A-bove thy deep and dream-less sleep the si-lent stars go by.
and praises sing to God the King, and peace to men on earth;

Yet in thy dark streets shin-eth the ev-er-last-ing light;
for Christ is born of Ma-ry; and, gath-ered all a-bove,

the hopes and fears of all the years are met in thee to-night.
while mor-tals sleep, the an-gels keep their watch of wond'ring love.

3. How silently, how silently,
   The wondrous gift is giv'n!
   So God imparts to human hearts
   The blessings of his heav'n.
   No ear may hear his coming;
   But in this world of sin,
   Where meek souls will receive him, still
   The dear Christ enters in.

4. O holy Child of Bethlehem,
   Descend to us, we pray;
   Cast out our sin, and enter in,
   Be born in us today.
   We hear the Christmas angels
   The great glad tidings tell:
   O come to us, abide with us,
   Our Lord Emmanuel.

ONCE IN ROYAL DAVID'S CITY

Words by C. F. ALEXANDER   Tune by H. J. GAUNTLETT

1. Once in roy-al Da-vid's ci-ty stood a low-ly cat-tle shed,
2. He came down to earth from hea-ven who is God and Lord of all,

where a mo-ther laid her Ba-by in a man-ger for his bed:
and his shel-ter was a sta-ble, and his cra-dle was a stall;

Ma-ry was that mo-ther mild, Je-sus Christ her lit-tle Child.
with the poor and mean and low-ly lived on earth our Sa-viour ho-ly.

3. And through all his wondrous childhood
He would honour and obey,
Love and watch the lowly maiden,
In whose gentle arms he lay:
Christian children all must be
Mild, obedient, good as he.

4. For he is our childhood's pattern,
Day by day like us he grew,
He was little, weak, and helpless,
Tears and smiles like us he knew:
And he feeleth for our sadness,
And he shareth in our gladness.

5. And our eyes at last shall see him,
Through his own redeeming love,
For that child so dear and gentle
Is our Lord in heaven above;
And he leads his children on
To the place where he is gone.

6. Not in that poor lowly stable,
With the oxen standing by,
We shall see him; but in heaven,
Set at God's right hand on high;
Where like stars his children crowned
All in white shall wait around.

PAST THREE A CLOCK

Words by G. R. WOODWARD

Traditional carol

2. Seraph quire singeth,
   Angel bell ringeth:
   Hark how they rime it,
   Time it, and chime it.

   Past three a clock,
   And a cold frosty morning;
   Past three a clock:
   Good morrow, masters all.

3. Mid-earth rejoices
   Hearing such voices
   Ne'ertofore so well
   Carolling *Nowell.*

   Past three a clock, etc.

4. Light out of star-land
   Leadeth from far land
   Princes, to meet him,
   Worship and greet him.

   Past three a clock, etc.

5. Myrrh from full coffer,
   Incense they offer:
   Nor is the golden
   Nugget withholden.

   Past three a clock, etc.

6. Thus they: I pray you,
   Up, sirs, nor stay you
   Till ye confess him
   Likewise, and bless him.

   Past three a clock, etc.

REJOICE AND BE MERRY

English traditional carol

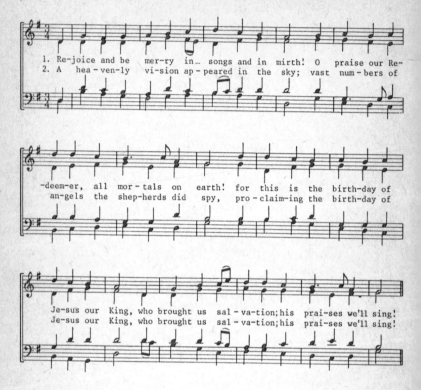

1. Re-joice and be mer-ry in songs and in mirth! O praise our Re-deemer, all mor-tals on earth! for this is the birth-day of Je-sus our King, who brought us sal-va-tion; his prai-ses we'll sing!

2. A hea-ven-ly vi-sion ap-peared in the sky; vast num-bers of an-gels the shep-herds did spy, pro-claim-ing the birth-day of Je-sus our King, who brought us sal-va-tion; his prai-ses we'll sing!

3. Likewise a bright star in the sky did appear,
Which led the wise men from the east to draw near;
They found the Messiah, sweet Jesus our King,
Who brought us salvation; his praises we'll sing!

4. And when they were come, they their treasures unfold,
And unto him offered myrrh, incense, and gold.
So blessed for ever be Jesus our King,
Who brought us salvation; his praises we'll sing.

REMEMBER, O THOU MAN

Tune by
THOMAS RAVENSCROFT

1. Re - mem - ber, O thou man, O thou man, O thou man, re - mem - ber,
2. Re - mem - ber God's good - ness, O thou man, O thou man, re - mem - ber

O thou man, thy time is spent: re - mem - ber, O thou man,
God's good - ness, and pro - mise made: re - mem - ber God's good - ness,

how thou cam'st to me then, and I did what I can, there - fore re - pent.
how his on - ly Son he sent, our sins for to re - dress: be not a - fraid.

3. The angels all did sing,
    O thou man, O thou man,
    The angels all did sing,
    On Sion hill:
    The angels all did sing
    Praises to our heav'nly King,
    And peace to man living,
    With right good will.

4. To Bethlem did they go,
    O thou man, O thou man,
    To Bethlem did they go,
    This thing to see:
    To Bethlem did they go,
    To see whether it was so,
    Whether Christ was born or no
    To set us free.

5. In Bethlem was he born
    O thou man, O thou man,
    In Bethlem was he born,
    For mankind dear:
    In Bethlem was he born,
    For us that were forlorn,
    And therefore took no scorn,
    Our sins to bear.

6. Give thanks to God always,
    O thou man, O thou man,
    Give thanks to God always,
    With hearts most jolly:
    Give thanks to God always
    Upon this blessèd day,
    Let all men sing and say,
    Holy, holy.

ROCKING
(LITTLE JESUS, SWEETLY SLEEP)

Translated by PERCY DEARMER

Czech carol

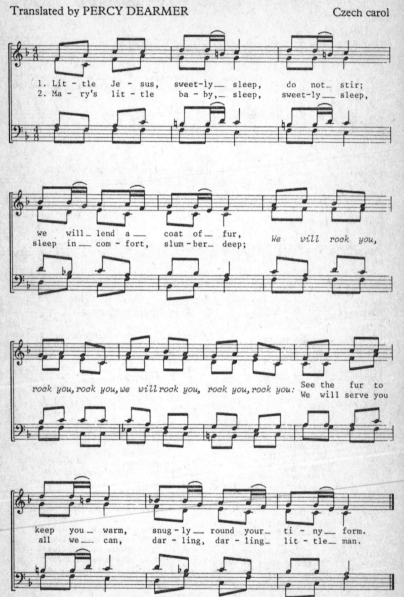

1. Lit - tle Je - sus, sweet-ly sleep, do not stir;
2. Ma - ry's lit - tle ba - by, sleep, sweet-ly sleep,

we will lend a coat of fur,
sleep in com - fort, slum - ber deep; *We will rock you,*

rock you, rock you, we will rock you, rock you, rock you: See the fur to
We will serve you

keep you warm, snug - ly round your ti - ny form.
all we can, dar - ling, dar - ling lit - tle man.

SANS DAY CAROL

(*NOW THE HOLLY BEARS A BERRY*)

Cornish traditional carol

SEE AMID THE WINTER'S SNOW

Tune by JOHN GOSS
(Slightly adapted)

1. See a - mid the win-ter's snow, born for us on earth be -low,_
2. Lo, wi - thin a man-ger lies_ he who built the star - ry skies;

see the ten - der Lamb ap - pears, pro-mis'd from e - ter-nal years.
he who, throned in height sub - lime, sits a - mid the che-ru - bim!

Hail! thou ev - er bless-ed morn! hail, re-demp-tion's hap-py_ dawn!

Sing thro' all Je - ru - sa - lem,_ Christ is born in Beth-le - hem.

3. Say, ye holy shepherds, say
   What your joyful news today;
   Wherefore have ye left your sheep
   On the lonely mountain steep?
   Hail! thou ever blessed morn! etc.

4. 'As we watch'd at dead of night,
   Lo, we saw a wondrous light;
   Angels singing 'Peace on earth,'
   Told us of a saviour's birth.'
   Hail! thou ever blessed morn! etc.

5. Sacred infant, all divine,
   What a tender love was thine;
   Thus to come from highest bliss
   Down to such a world as this!
   Hail! thou ever blessed morn! etc.

6. Teach, O teach us, holy Child,
   By thy face so meek and mild,
   Teach us to resemble thee,
   In thy sweet humility!
   Hail! thou ever blessed morn! etc.

SHEPHERDS LEFT THEIR FLOCKS

(QUEM PASTORES LAUDAVERE)

Fourteenth-century German tune

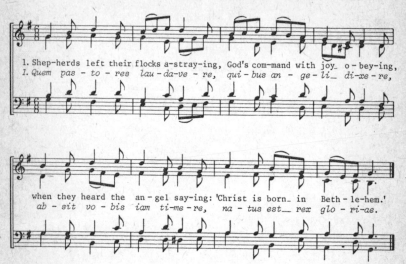

1. Shep-herds left their flocks a-stray-ing, God's com-mand with joy o-bey-ing,
1. *Quem pas - to - res lau - da - ve - re, qui-bus an - ge - li di - xe - re,*

when they heard the an - gel say-ing: 'Christ is born in Beth - le-hem.'
ab - sit vo - bis iam ti-me - re, na - tus est rex glo - ri-ae.

2. Wise men came from far, and saw him:
   Knelt in homage to adore him;
   Precious gifts they laid before him:
   Gold and frankincense and myrrh.

2. *Ad quem magi ambulabant,*
   Aurum, thus, myrrham portabant,
   Immolabant haec sincere
   Nato regi gloriae.

3. Let us now in ev'ry nation
   Sing his praise with exultation.
   All the world shall find salvation
   In the birth of Mary's Son.

3. *Christo regi, Deo nato,*
   Per Mariam nobis dato,
   Merito resonet vere
   Laus, honor et gloria.

SILENT NIGHT

Translated by
DAVID WILLCOCKS

Tune by FRANZ GRUBER

Si - lent night, ho - ly night,
si - lent, ho - ly,

1. All is dark, —
2. Shep herds first —
3. God's own Son, —

save the light — shi - ning where the mo - ther mild
saw the sight, — heard the an - gel - song 'Al - le - lu - ya,'
oh how bright — shines the love in the ho - ly face,

watch - es ov - er the ho - ly Child. Sleep in hea - ven - ly
loud pro - claim - ing near — and far: Christ our Sa - viour is
shines the light of re - demp - tion and grace, Christ th'in - car - nate

peace, — sleep — in hea - ven - ly peace.
here, — Christ — our Sa - viour is here.
God, — Christ — th'in - car - nate God.

87

SING ALOUD ON THIS DAY

(PERSONENT HODIE)

Translated by
JOHN A. PARKINSON

Fourteenth-century German tune

1. Sing a-loud on this day! Child-ren all raise the lay.
2. Per-so-nent ho-di-e vo-ces pu - er-u-lae,

Cheer-ful-ly we and they hast-en to a - dore thee,
lau-dan-tes ju-cun-de qui no-bis est na - tus,

sent from high-est glo-ry, for us born, born, born, for us born,
sum-mo De-o da-tus, et de vir- vir-vir, et de vir-

born, born, for us born__ on this morn__ of the Vir-gin Ma-ry.
vir- vir, et de vir - gi-ne-o____ ven-tre pro-cre-a - tus.

for us born__ on this morn
et de vir - - gi-ne-o

2. Now a child he is born,
   Swathing bands him adorn,
   Manger bed he'll not scorn,
   Ox and ass are near him;
   We as Lord revere him,
   And the vain, vain, vain,
   And the vain, vain, vain,
   And the vain powers of hell
   Spoiled of prey now fear him.

3. From the far Orient
   Guiding star wise men sent;
   Him to seek their intent,
   Lord of all creation;
   Kneel in adoration.
   Gifts of gold, gold, gold,
   Gifts of gold, gold, gold,
   Gifts of gold, frankincense,
   Myrrh for their oblation.

4. All must join him to praise;
   Men and boys voices raise
   On this day of all days;
   Angel voices ringing,
   Christmas tidings bringing.
   Join we all, all, all,
   Join we all, all, all,
   Join we all, 'Gloria
   In excelsis' singing.

2. *In mundo nascitur,*
   Pannis involvitur,
   Praesepi ponitur
   Stabulo brutorum
   Rector supernorum.
   Perdidit, dit, dit,
   Perdidit, dit, dit,
   Perdidit spolia
   Princeps infernorum.

3. *Magi tres venerunt,*
   Parvulum inquirunt,
   Bethlehem adeunt,
   Stellulam sequendo,
   Ipsum adorando,
   Aurum, thus, thus, thus,
   Aurum, thus, thus, thus,
   Aurum, thus, et myrrham
   Ei offerendo.

4. *Omnes clericuli,*
   Pariter pueri,
   Cantent ut angeli:
   Advenisti mundo,
   Laudes tibi fundo.
   Ideo, o, o,
   Ideo, o, o,
   Ideo, gloria
   In excelsis Deo!

SUSSEX CAROL

(ON CHRISTMAS NIGHT ALL CHRISTIANS SING)

English traditional carol

1. On Christ-mas night all Christ-ians sing, to hear the news the
2. Then why should men on earth be so sad, since our Re-deem-er

an - gels bring,
made us glad,

Ah,

on Christ-mas night all Christ - ians sing, to
then why should men on earth be so sad, since

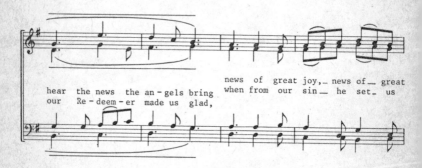

news of great joy,— news of— great
when from our sin— he set— us

hear the news the an-gels bring
our Re-deem-er made us glad,

mirth,— news of our mer - ci-ful— King's birth.
free,— all for to gain our li - ber - ty?

3. *Sop.* When sin departs before his grace,
   Then life and health come in its place;
   Ten. When sin departs before his grace,
   Then life and health come in its place;
   All Angels and men with joy may sing,
   All for to see the new-born King.

4. *Sop.* All out of darkness we have light,
   Which made the angels sing this night:
   Ten. All out of darkness we have light,
   Which made the angels sing this night:
   All 'Glory to God and peace to men,
   Now and for evermore. Amen.'

THE FIRST NOWELL

English traditional carol

1. The first Nowell the angel did say, was to certain poor
2. They looked up and saw a star, shining in the

shepherds in fields as they lay; in fields where they lay
east, beyond them far, and to the earth it

keeping their sheep, on a cold winter's night that was so deep.
gave great light, and so it continued both day and night.

Nowell, Nowell, Nowell, Nowell,

born is the King of Israel.

3. And by the light of that same star,
   Three wise men came from country far;
   To seek for a king was their intent,
   And to follow the star wherever it went.
   Nowell, etc.

4. This star drew nigh to the north-west,
   O'er Bethlehem it took its rest,
   And there it did both stop and stay
   Right over the place where Jesus lay.
   Nowell, etc.

5. Then entered in those wise men three,
   Full rev'rently upon their knee,
   And offer'd there, in his presence,
   Their gold, and myrrh, and frankincense.
   Nowell, etc.

6. Then let us all with one accord
   Sing praises to our heav'nly Lord,
   That hath made heav'n and earth of nought,
   And with his blood mankind hath bought.
   Nowell, etc.

THE HOLLY AND THE IVY

English traditional carol

1. The hol-ly and the i - vy, when they are both full grown;
of _ all the trees that are in the wood the_ hol-ly bears the crown.
the ri-sing of the sun, _ the run-ning of the deer,
O the ri-sing of the sun _ and the run-ning of the deer,
the_ play-ing of the mer-ry or - gan, sweet sing-ing in the choir.

2. The holly bears a blossom
   As white as any flower;
   And Mary bore sweet Jesus Christ
   To be our sweet Saviour.

3. The holly bears a berry
   As red as any blood;
   And Mary bore sweet Jesus Christ
   To do poor sinners good.

4. The holly bears a prickle
   As sharp as any thorn;
   And Mary bore sweet Jesus Christ
   On Christmas Day in the morn.

5. The holly bears a bark
   As bitt'r as any gall;
   And Mary bore sweet Jesus Christ
   For to redeem us all.

THE INFANT KING

(SING LULLABY)

Words by S. BARING-GOULD

Basque carol

1. Sing lul-la-by! Lul-la-by ba-by, now re-clin-ing, sing lul-la-by!
2. Sing lul-la-by! Lul-la-by ba-by, now a-sleep-ing, sing lul-la-by!

Hush, do not wake the In-fant King. An-gels are watch-ing, stars are
Hush, do not wake the In-fant King. Soon will come sor-row with the

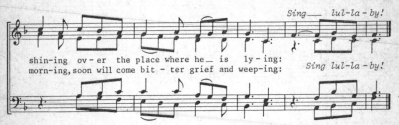

Sing — lul-la-by!

shin-ing ov-er the place where he is ly-ing:
morn-ing, soon will come bit-ter grief and weep-ing: Sing lul-la-by!

3. *Sing lullaby!*
   Lullaby baby, now a-dozing,
   Sing lullaby!
   Hush, do not wake the Infant King.
   Soon comes the cross, the nails, the piercing,
   Then in the grave at last reposing:
   Sing lullaby!

4. *Sing lullaby!*
   Lullaby! is the babe a-waking?
   Sing lullaby!
   Hush, do not wake the Infant King.
   Dreaming of Easter, gladsome morning,
   Conquering death, its bondage breaking:
   Sing lullaby!

THE SEVEN JOYS

(THE FIRST GOOD JOY THAT MARY HAD)

English traditional carol

The first good joy that Ma - ry had, it was the joy of one; —

to see the bless-ed Je - sus Christ, when he was first her son: —

when he was first her son, good Lord; and hap - py we may be: _____

Praise Fa - ther, Son and Ho - ly Ghost to all e - ter - ni - ty. —

2. The next good joy that Mary had,
   It was the joy of two;
   To see her own son Jesus Christ
   Making the lame to go:
   Making the lame to go, good Lord,
   And happy may we be:
   Praise Father, etc.

3. The next good joy that Mary had,
   It was the joy of three;
   To see her own son Jesus Christ
   Making the blind to see:
   Making the blind to see, good Lord,
   And happy may we be:
   Praise Father, etc.

4. The next good joy that Mary had,
   It was the joy of four;
   To see her own son Jesus Christ
   Reading the bible o'er:
   Reading the bible o'er, good Lord,
   And happy may we be:
   Praise Father, etc.

5. The next good joy that Mary had,
   It was the joy of five;
   To see her own son Jesus Christ
   Bringing the dead alive:
   Bringing the dead alive, good Lord,
   And happy may we be:
   Praise Father, etc.

6. The next good joy that Mary had,
   It was the joy of six;
   To see her own son Jesus Christ
   Upon the crucifix:
   Upon the crucifix, good Lord;
   And happy may we be:
   Praise Father, etc.

7. The next good joy that Mary had,
   It was the joy of seven;
   To see her own son Jesus Christ
   Ascending into heaven:
   Ascending into heaven, good Lord;
   And happy we may be:
   Praise Father, etc.

THE TWELVE DAYS OF CHRISTMAS

(ON THE FIRST DAY OF CHRISTMAS)

English traditional carol

Sing appropriate number of day, and then cut from ✳ *to appropriate figure.*

ten lords a-leap-ing, nine la-dies danc-ing, eight maids a-milk-ing,
ten   nine   eight

sev'n swans a-swim-ming, six geese a-lay-ing, five gold_
sev'n   six

rings, __ four __ call-ing birds, three French hens,

two __ tur-tle doves, and a par-tridge in a pear-tree.

THIS ENDRIS NIGHT

Words fifteenth century
Anon.

VERSION I

1. This en-dris night I saw a sight, a star as bright as day;
2. This love-ly la - dy sat and sung, and to her child did say:

and ev - er a-mong, a mai - den sung, 'Lul - lay, by by, lul - lay.'
'My son, my bro-ther, fa - ther, dear, why liest thou thus in hay?'

VERSION II (Melody in Alto) *for alternate verses*

Ah,   Ah,

3. 'My sweet-est bird, thus,'tis re-quired, though thou be King ve - ray;

Ah,   Ah,

Ah,   Ah,

but nev-er-the-less I will not cease to sing, By by, lul - lay.'

Ah,   Ah,

If preferred, the whole carol may be sung to Version I.

3. 'My sweetest bird, thus 'tis required,
Though thou be king veray;
But nevertheless I will not cease
To sing, By by, lullay.'

4. The child then spake in his talking,
And to his mother said:
'Yea, I am known as heaven-king,
In crib though I be laid;

5. 'For angels bright down to me light:
Thou knowest 'tis no nay:
And for that sight thou may'st delight
To sing, By by, lullay.'

6. 'Now, sweet son, since thou art a king,
Why art thou laid in stall?
Why dost not order thy bedding
In some great kingès hall?

7. 'Methinks 'tis right that king or knight
Should lie in good array:
And then among, it were no wrong
To sing, By by, lullay.'

8. 'Mary mother, I am thy child,
Though I be laid in stall;
For lords and dukes shall worship me,
And so shall kingès all.

9. 'Ye shall well see that kingès three
Shall come on this twelfth day.
For this behest give me thy breast,
And sing, By by, lullay.'

10. 'Now tell, sweet son, I thee do pray,
Thou art my love and dear –
How should I keep thee to thy pay,
And make thee glad of cheer?

11. 'For all thy will I would fulfil –
Thou knowest well, in fay;
And for all this I will thee kiss,
And sing, By by, lullay.'

12. 'My dear mother, when time it be,
Take thou me up on loft,
And set me then upon thy knee,
And handle me full soft;

13. 'And in thy arm thou hold me warm,
And keep me night and day,
And if I weep, and may not sleep,
Thou sing, By by, lullay.'

14. 'Now, sweet son, since it is come so,
That all is at thy will,
I pray thee grant to me a boon,
If it be right and skill, –

15. 'That child or man, who will or can
Be merry on my day,
To bliss thou bring – and I shall sing,
Lullay, by by, lullay.'

This endris night – the other night; *ever among* – every now and then;
veray – true; *light* – alight; *no nay* – not to be denied; *pay* – satisfaction;
in fay – in faith; *skill* – reasonable.

THE THREE KINGS

(THREE KINGS FROM PERSIAN LANDS)

Words by H. N. BATE

Tune by PETER CORNELIUS
Adapted

1. Three kings from Per - sian lands a - far to Jor-dan fol-low the point-ing star: and this the quest of the tra-vel-lers three, where the new-born King of the Jews may be. Full roy-al gifts they bear for the King; gold, in-cense, myrrh are their of - fer-ing. ___ 2. The star shines

How bright-ly shines the morn - ing star! with grace and truth from heav'n a - far our Jes - se tree now ___ blow - - eth.

out— with a stead-fast ray; the kings to Beth-le-hem

Of Ja - cob's stem and

make their way, and there in wor-ship they bend the— knee, as Ma-ry's

Da - vid's line, for thee, my

child— in .her— lap they see; their roy-al gifts they show to the

Bride - groom, King di - vine, my

King: gold, in-cense, myrrh are their of-fer-ing.— Thou child of man,

soul — with love— o'er - flow - eth. Thy— word,

TOMORROW SHALL BE MY DANCING DAY

English traditional carol

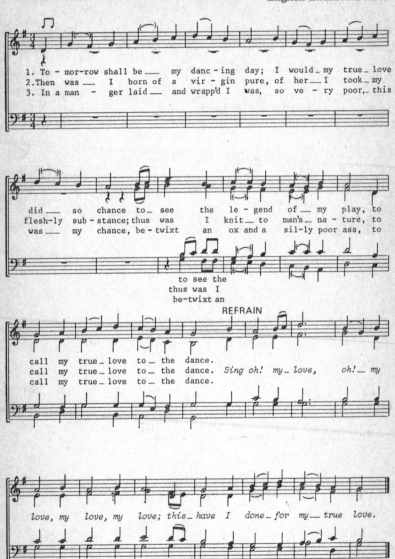

1. To-mor-row shall be __ my danc-ing day; I would __ my true __ love
2. Then was __ I born of a vir-gin pure, of her __ I took __ my
3. In a man - ger laid __ and wrapp'd I was, so ve - ry poor, __ this

did __ so chance to __ see the le - gend of __ my play, to
flesh-ly sub - stance; thus was I knit __ to man's __ na - ture, to
was __ my chance, be - twixt an ox and a sil - ly poor ass, to

to see the
thus was I
be - twixt an

REFRAIN

call my true __ love to __ the dance.
call my true __ love to __ the dance. *Sing oh! my __ love, oh! __ my*
call my true __ love to __ the dance.

love, my love, my love; this __ have I done __ for my __ true love.

105

UNTO US IS BORN A SON

Sixteenth-century tune

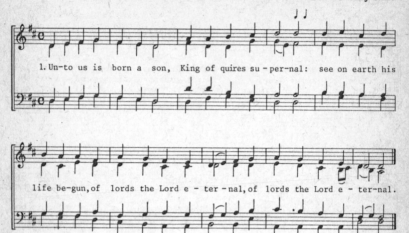

1. Un-to us is born a son, King of quires su-per-nal: see on earth his life be-gun, of lords the Lord e-ter-nal, of lords the Lord e-ter-nal.

2. Christ, from heav'n descending low,
   Comes on earth a stranger;
   Ox and ass their owner know,
   Becradled in the manger.

3. This did Herod sore affray,
   And grievously bewilder,
   So he gave the word to slay,
   And slew the little childer.

4. Of his love and mercy mild
   This the Christmas story;
   And O that Mary's gentle child
   Might lead us up to glory.

5. O and A, and A and O,
   Cum cantibus in choro,
   Let our merry organ go,
   Benedicamus Domino.

UP! GOOD CHRISTEN FOLK

(*DING DONG DING!*)

Words by G. R. WOODWARD

Sixteenth-century tune

Ding dong ding! Ding-a-dong-a-ding! Ding dong, ding dong: Ding-a-dong-ding!

Up! good Christen folk, and list-en how the mer-ry church — bells ring,
Tell the sto-ry how from glo-ry God came down at Christ — mas-tide,

and from stee-ple bid good peo-ple come a-dore the new — born King:
bring-ing glad-ness, cha-sing sad-ness, show'ring blessings far — and wide,

born of — mo-ther, blest o'er o-ther, *ex Ma-ri-a vir-gi-ne,*

in a sta-ble ('tis no fa-ble), *Chris-tus na-tus ho — di-e.*

WE THREE KINGS

Words and tune by
J. H. HOPKINS

1.We three kings of o-ri-ent are; bear-ing gifts we tra-verse a-far field and foun-tain, moor and moun-tain, fol-low-ing yon-der star:

O — star of won-der, star of night, star with roy-al beau-ty bright, west-ward lead-ing, still pro-ceed-ing, guide us to thy per-fect light.

(Melchior)

2. Born a king on Bethlehem plain,
   Gold I bring, to crown him again,
   King for ever, ceasing never,
   Over us all to reign:

   O star of wonder, etc.

(Caspar)

3. Frankincense to offer have I,
   Incense owns a deity nigh;
   Prayer and praising, all men raising,
   Worship him, God most high:

   O star of wonder, etc.

(Balthazar)

4. Myrrh is mine; its bitter perfume
   Breathes a life of gathering gloom;
   Sorrowing, sighing, bleeding, dying,
   Sealed in the stone-cold tomb:

   O star of wonder, etc.

(All)

5. Glorious now behold him arise,
   King and God and sacrifice,
   Alleluya, alleluya,
   Earth to the heavens replies:

   O star of wonder, etc.

WHENCE IS THAT GOODLY FRAGRANCE?

(QUELLE EST CETTE ODEUR AGREABLE?)

Translated by A. B. RAMSAY
V.4 translated by
DAVID WILLCOCKS

French traditional carol

1. Whence is that good-ly fra-grance flow-ing, steal-ing our
1. Quelle est cette o-deur a-gré-a-ble, ber-gers, qui

sen-ses all a-way? Nev-er the like did come a-
ra-vit tous nos sens? S'ex-ha-le-t-il rien de sem-

Fine

-blow-ing, shep-herds, in flow-'ry fields in May,
-bla-ble au mi-lieu des fleurs du prin-temps?

D.C.

2. What is that light so brilliant breaking
   Here in the night across our eyes?
   Never so bright, the day-star waking,
   Started to climb the morning skies!

3. Bethlehem! there in manger lying,
   Find your Redeemer, haste away,
   Run ye with eager footsteps hieing!
   Worship the Saviour born today.

4. Praise to the Lord of all creation,
   Glory to God the fount of grace;
   May peace abide in ev'ry nation,
   Goodwill in men of ev'ry race.

2. *Mais quelle éclatante lumière*
   Dans la nuit vient frapper nos yeux!
   L'astre du jour, dans sa carrière,
   Fût-il jamais si radieux?

3. *A Bethléem, dans une crèche,*
   Il vient de vous naître un Sauveur;
   Allons, que rien ne vous empêche
   D'adorer votre rédempteur.

4. *Dieu tout-puissant, gloire éternelle*
   Vous soit rendue jusqu'aux cieux;
   Que la paix soit universelle,
   Que la grâce abonde en tous lieux.

WHILE SHEPHERDS WATCHED

Words by NAHUM TATE

Este's Psalter, sixteenth century

1. While shep – herds watched their flocks by night, all
2. 'Fear not,' said he, (for migh – ty dread had

seat – ed on the ground, the an – gel of the
seized their troub – led mind); 'glad ti – dings of great

Lord came down, and glo – ry shone a – round.
joy I bring to you and all man – kind.

3. 'To you in David's town this day
   Is born of David's line
   A Saviour, who is Christ the Lord;
   And this shall be the sign:

4. 'The heavenly Babe you there shall find
   To human view displayed,
   All meanly wrapped in swathing bands,
   And in a manger laid.'

5. Thus spake the Seraph; and forthwith
   Appeared a shining throng
   Of angels praising God, who thus
   Addressed their joyful song:

6. 'All glory be to God on high,
   And on the earth be peace;
   Good-will henceforth from heaven to men
   Begin and never cease.'

WILLIE, TAKE YOUR LITTLE DRUM

(*PATAPAN*)

Translated by PERCY DEARMER

Burgundian tune